I0462185

# Math Mammoth
# Grade 1-B Worktext

*By Maria Miller*

Copyright 2026 Taina Maria Miller

ISBN 978-1-954379-38-1

2026 Edition

All rights reserved. No part of this book may be reproduced or transmitted in any form or by any means, electronic or mechanical, or by any information storage and retrieval system, without permission in writing from the author.

**Copying permission:** For having purchased this book, the copyright owner grants to the teacher-purchaser a limited permission to reproduce this material for use with his or her students. In other words, the teacher-purchaser MAY make copies of the pages, or an electronic copy of the PDF file, and provide them at no cost to the students he or she is actually teaching, but not to students of other teachers. This permission also extends to the spouse of the purchaser, for the purpose of providing copies for the children in the same family. Sharing the file with anyone else, whether via the Internet or other media, is strictly prohibited.

No permission is granted for resale of the material.

The copyright holder also grants permission to the purchaser to make electronic copies of the material for back-up purposes.

If you have other needs, such as licensing for a school or tutoring center, please contact the author at
https://www.MathMammoth.com/contact

# Contents

## Chapter 8: Adding and Subtracting Within 0-100

## Chapter 9: Graphs

## Chapter 10: Coins

# Foreword

Math Mammoth Grade 1 comprises a complete math curriculum for the first grade mathematics studies. The curriculum meets the Common Core standards.

The main areas of study for Math Mammoth Grade 1 are:

1. The concepts of addition and subtraction, strategies for addition and subtraction facts, and addition and subtraction word problems;

2. Developing understanding of place value for two-digit numbers;

3. Developing understanding and some basic strategies for two-digit addition and subtraction.

Additional topics we study are telling time (whole and half hours), geometric shapes, measurement, and counting coins.

This book, the 1-B worktext, covers addition and subtraction facts (chapter 5), shapes and fractions (chapter 6), measurement (chapter 7), adding and subtracting two-digit numbers (chapter 8), graphs (chapter 9), and counting coins (chapter 10). The book 1-A covers addition and subtraction within 0-10, word problems, place value with two-digit numbers, and time.

I heartily recommend that you read the full user guide in the following pages.

*I wish you success in teaching math!*

*Maria Miller, the author*

# User Guide

Note: You can also find the information that follows online, at https://www.mathmammoth.com/userguides/ .

The Common Core Standards documentation is available at:
https://www.mathmammoth.com/preview/standards/MM-CCS-Grade1-2026.pdf

## Basic principles in using Math Mammoth Complete Curriculum

Math Mammoth is mastery-based, which means it concentrates on a few major topics at a time, in order to study them in depth. The two books (parts A and B) are like a "framework", but you still have a lot of liberty in planning your child's studies. You can even use it in a *spiral* manner, if you prefer. Simply have your student study in 2-3 chapters simultaneously. In first grade, I suggest studying chapters 1-3 in order, but you can be flexible with the other chapters and schedule them earlier or later.

Math Mammoth is not a scripted curriculum. In other words, it is not spelling out in exact detail what the teacher is to do or say. Instead, Math Mammoth gives you, the teacher, various tools for teaching:

- **The two student worktexts** (parts A and B) contain all the lesson material and exercises. They include the explanations of the concepts (the teaching part) in blue boxes. The worktexts also contain some advice for the teacher in the "Introduction" of each chapter.

  The teacher can read the teaching part of each lesson before the lesson, or read and study it together with the student in the lesson, or let the student read and study on his own. If you are a classroom teacher, you can copy the examples from the "blue teaching boxes" to the board and go through them on the board.

- There are hundreds of **videos** matched to the curriculum available at https://www.mathmammoth.com/videos/ . There isn't a video for every lesson, but there are dozens of videos for each grade level. You can simply have the author teach your child or student!

- Don't automatically assign all the exercises. Use your judgment, trying to assign just enough for your student's needs. You can use the skipped exercises later for review. For most students, I recommend to start out by assigning about half of the available exercises. Adjust as necessary.

- Each chapter introduction contains a **list of links to various free online games** and activities. These games can be used to supplement the math lessons, for learning math facts, or just for some fun.

- The student books contain some **mixed review lessons**, and the curriculum also provides you with additional **cumulative review lessons**.

- There is a **chapter test** for each chapter of the curriculum, and a comprehensive end-of-year test.

- The **worksheet maker** allows you to make additional worksheets for most calculation-type topics in the curriculum. This is a single html file. You will need Internet access to be able to use it.

- You can use the free online exercises at https://www.mathmammoth.com/practice/
  This is an expanding section of the site, so check often to see what new topics we are adding to it!

- Some grade levels have **cut-outs** to make fraction manipulatives or geometric solids.

- The answer key is included when you purchase the digital version (the download). If you purchase the printed version, the answer key is available as a separate book.

## How to get started

Have ready the first lesson from the student worktext. Go over the first teaching part (within the blue boxes) together with your child. Go through a few of the first exercises together, and then assign some problems for your child to do on their own.

Repeat this if the lesson has other blue teaching boxes. Naturally, you can also use the videos at https://www.mathmammoth.com/videos/

Many students can eventually study the lessons completely on their own — the curriculum becomes self-teaching. However, students definitely vary in how much they need someone to be there to actually teach them.

## Pacing the curriculum

Each chapter introduction contains a suggested pacing guide for that chapter. You will see a summary on the right. (This summary does not include the optional lessons, nor time for the optional tests.)

Most lessons are 2 pages long, intended for one day. Some lessons are 3 pages, again intended for one day but you can take two if needed. There are also a few optional lessons, not included in the tables on the right.

It can also be helpful to calculate a general guideline as to how many pages per week the student should cover in order to go through the curriculum in one school year.

| Worktext 1-A | | Worktext 1-B | |
|---|---|---|---|
| Chapter 0 | 6 days | Chapter 5 | 15 days |
| Chapter 1 | 22 days | Chapter 6 | 12 days |
| Chapter 2 | 19 days | Chapter 7 | 7 days |
| Chapter 3 | 17 days | Chapter 8 | 24 days |
| Chapter 4 | 6 days | Chapter 9 | 5 days |
| **TOTAL** | 70 days | Chapter 10 | 9 days |
| | | **TOTAL** | 72 days |

The table below lists how many pages there are for the student to finish in this particular grade level, and gives you a guideline for how many pages per day to finish, assuming a 170-day (34-week) school year. The page count in the table below *includes* the optional lessons.

**Example:**

| Grade level | School days | Days for tests and reviews | Lesson pages | Days for the student book | Pages to study per day | Pages to study per week |
|---|---|---|---|---|---|---|
| 1-A | 83 | 8 | 149 | 75 | 2 | 10 |
| 1-B | 87 | 10 | 151 | 77 | 2 | 10 |
| Grade 1 total | 170 | 18 | 300 | 152 | 2 | 10 |

The table below is for you to fill in. Allow several days for tests and additional review before tests — I suggest at least twice the number of chapters in the curriculum. Then, to get a count of "pages to study per day", **divide the number of lesson pages by the number of days for the student book**. Lastly, multiply this number by 5 to get the approximate page count to cover in a week.

| Grade level | Number of school days | Days for tests and reviews | Lesson pages | Days for the student book | Pages to study per day | Pages to study per week |
|---|---|---|---|---|---|---|
| 1-A | | | 149 | | | |
| 1-B | | | 151 | | | |
| Grade 1 total | | | 300 | | | |

Now, something important. Whenever the curriculum has lots of similar practice problems (a large set of problems), feel free to **only assign 1/2 or 2/3 of those problems**. If your student gets it with less amount of exercises, then that is perfect! If not, you can always assign the rest of the problems for some other day. In fact, you could even use these unassigned problems the next week or next month for some additional review.

In general, 1st-2nd graders might spend 25-40 minutes a day on math. Third-fourth graders might spend 30-60 minutes a day. Fifth-sixth graders might spend 45-75 minutes a day. If your student finds math enjoyable, they can of course spend more time with it! However, it is not good to drag out the lessons on a regular basis, because that can then affect the student's attitude towards math.

## Working space, the usage of additional paper, and mental math

The curriculum generally includes working space directly on the page for students to work out the problems. However, feel free to let your students use extra paper when necessary. They can use it, not only for the "long" algorithms (where you line up numbers to add, subtract, multiply, and divide), but also to draw diagrams and pictures to help organize their thoughts. Some students won't need the additional space (and may resist the thought of extra paper), while some will benefit from it. Use your discretion.

Some exercises don't have any working space, but just an empty line for the answer (e.g. 200 + _____ = 1,000). Typically, I have intended that such exercises be done using *mental math*.

However, there are some students who struggle with mental math (often this is because of not having studied and used it in the past). As always, the teacher has the final say (not me!) as to how to approach the exercises and how to use the curriculum. We do want to prevent extreme frustration (to the point of tears). The goal is always to provide SOME challenge, but not too much, and to let students experience success enough so that they can continue to enjoy learning math.

Students struggling with mental math will probably benefit from studying the basic principles of mental calculations from the earlier levels of Math Mammoth curriculum. To do so, look for lessons that list mental math strategies. They are taught in the chapters about addition, subtraction, place value, multiplication, and division. My article at https://www.mathmammoth.com/lessons/practical_tips_mental_math also gives you a summary of some of those principles.

## Using tests

For each chapter, there is a **chapter test**, which can be administered right after studying the chapter. **The tests are optional.** Some families might prefer not to give tests at all. The main reason for the tests is for diagnostic purposes, and for record keeping. These tests are not aligned or matched to any standards.

In the digital version of the curriculum, the tests are provided as PDF files. You can edit them (such as to change the numbers in them) to provide a different test using PDF apps that have editing capabilities. You can even use the annotation tools (such as text boxes) available in most PDF apps. Remember to save the edited file under a different file name, or you will lose the original.

The end-of-year test is best administered as a diagnostic or assessment test, which will tell you how well the student remembers and has mastered the mathematics content of the entire grade level.

## Using cumulative reviews and the worksheet maker

The student books contain mixed review lessons which review concepts from earlier chapters. The curriculum also comes with additional cumulative review lessons, which are just like the mixed review lessons in the student books, with a mix of problems covering various topics. These are found in their own folder in the digital version, and in the Tests & Cumulative Reviews book in the print version.

The cumulative reviews are optional; use them as needed. They are named indicating which chapters of the main curriculum the problems in the review come from. For example, "Cumulative Review, Chapter 4" includes problems that cover topics from chapters 1-4.

Both the mixed and cumulative reviews allow you to spot areas that the student has not grasped well or has forgotten. When you find such a topic or concept, you have several options:

1. Check if the worksheet maker lets you make worksheets for that topic.

2. Check for any online games and resources in the Introduction part of the particular chapter in which this topic or concept was taught.

3. If you have the digital version, you could reprint the lesson from the student worktext, and have the student restudy that.

4. Perhaps you only assigned 1/2 or 2/3 of the exercise sets in the student book at first, and can now use the remaining exercises.

5. Check if our online practice area at https://www.mathmammoth.com/practice/ has something for that topic.

6. Khan Academy has free online exercises, articles, and videos for most any math topic imaginable.

## Concerning challenging word problems and puzzles

While this is not absolutely necessary, I heartily recommend supplementing Math Mammoth with challenging word problems and puzzles. You could do that once a month, for example, or more often if the student enjoys it.

The goal of challenging story problems and puzzles is to **develop the student's logical and abstract thinking and mental discipline**. I recommend starting these in fourth grade, at the latest. Then, students are able to read the problems on their own and have developed mathematical knowledge in many different areas. Of course I am not discouraging students from doing such in earlier grades, either.

Math Mammoth curriculum contains lots of word problems, and they are usually multi-step problems. Several of the lessons utilize a bar model for solving problems. Even so, the problems I have created are usually tied to a specific concept or concepts. I feel students can benefit from solving problems and puzzles that require them to think "out of the box" or are just different from the ones I have written.

I recommend you use the free Math Stars problem-solving newsletters as one of the main resources for puzzles and challenging problems:

**Math Stars Problem Solving Newsletter (grades 1-8)**
**https://www.homeschoolmath.net/teaching/math-stars.php**

I have also compiled a list of other resources for problem solving practice, which you can access at this link:

**https://l.mathmammoth.com/challengingproblems**

Another idea: you can find puzzles online by searching for "brain puzzles for kids," "logic puzzles for kids" or "brain teasers for kids."

## Frequently asked questions and contacting us

If you have more questions, please first check the FAQ at https://www.mathmammoth.com/faq-lightblue

If the FAQ does not cover your question, you can then contact us using the contact form at the Math Mammoth.com website.

# Chapter 5: Addition and Subtraction Facts
## Introduction

This chapter provides lots of practice for learning and memorizing the basic addition and subtraction facts with numbers from 0 to 10. The Common Core Standards require children in the first grade to demonstrate fluency in addition and subtraction with numbers up to 10, and we aim for that goal here.

Since this chapter is repetitive, consider studying it simultaneously with some other section of the curriculum, such as shapes, measuring, graphs, and/or counting coins. For example, the child could study shapes and this chapter each day, or study the two different chapters on alternate days. (This is not compulsory but just a suggestion to "mix things up" in a somewhat spiral fashion.)

Each of the lessons titled *Addition and Subtraction Facts with...* approaches the fact memorization from the concept of *fact families*, which makes the process logical and structured. For example, we study the fact families where the sum is 7, all in one lesson. This means the different sums that make seven ($0 + 7$, $1 + 6$, $2 + 5$, $3 + 4$) and their corresponding subtraction facts are practiced together.

Many children may not need all the practice problems provided, so don't assign all of them by default. Use your judgment, and only assign a certain portion, such as half of them, at first. (The rest of them can be used later as a review.) Adjust as necessary.

Alongside the lessons, you can use math games and/or flashcards to reinforce the facts. You will find a list of some games below.

While your child or students do not absolutely have to learn these facts by heart while studying this chapter, it is advisable to learn them fairly well. Mathematics builds upon previously learned concepts and facts, and learning addition and subtraction facts is very important for later study, such as when students learn to add a two-digit number and a single digit number (e.g. $24 + 5$, in chapter 8). However, if the child has not memorized these facts before the end of the chapter, don't worry. Go on with the curriculum, but keep practicing the facts with games, worksheets, drills, *etc.*

Besides practicing the facts with the help of fact families, the student will also solve word problems, fill in number patterns, get used to a symbol representing an unknown number, compare number expressions (such as $5 - 2$ and $2 + 5$), and subtract more than one number at a time.

As a friendly reminder, there are videos matched to the curriculum at https://www.mathmammoth.com/videos. Choose Grade 1.

**Good Mathematical Practices**

- As we return to addition and subtraction, there are again lots of word problems to solve. Some of them will ask the student to choose or write an equation that matches the problem. This is the beginning stage of *mathematical modeling*: using mathematics to model real-life situations. Writing an equation for a problem is simple at this stage (e.g. $2 + 3 = 5$) but it is a separate skill from just solving the problem.

  Essentially, the student will be showing their work for the problem. This will probably take some time to master, so don't worry if this is challenging for your child or student at this point. If so, ask them sometimes to write down the calculation even for word problems where the instruction doesn't explicitly state so.

**Math Talks**

A friendly reminder... check out our math-inspired real-life photographs that you can use for "math talks" about math in real life. Try to also find objects and scenes around you that can be used in this manner.

https://www.mathmammoth.com/MathTalks

## Pacing Suggestion for Chapter 5

Please add one day to the pacing for the test if you will use it.

| The Lessons in Chapter 5 | page | span | suggested pacing | your pacing |
|---|---|---|---|---|
| Addition and Subtraction Facts with 4 and 5 .................. | 17 | *2 pages* | 1 day | |
| Addition and Subtraction Facts with 6 ........................... | 19 | *2 pages* | 1 day | |
| Word Problems and Symbols ....................................... | 21 | *2 pages* | 1 day | |
| Addition and Subtraction Facts with 7 ........................... | 23 | *2 pages* | 1 day | |
| Addition and Subtraction Facts with 8 ........................... | 25 | *2 pages* | 1 day | |
| Review—Facts with 6, 7, and 8 ................................... | 27 | *2 pages* | 1 day | |
| Comparisons and Word Problems ................................. | 29 | *2 pages* | 1 day | |
| Addition and Subtraction Facts with 9 ........................... | 31 | *2 pages* | 1 day | |
| More Practice ............................................................. | 33 | *2 pages* | 1 day | |
| Addition and Subtraction Facts with 10 ......................... | 35 | *2 pages* | 1 day | |
| Review of Facts with 9 and 10 .................................... | 37 | *2 pages* | 1 day | |
| Subtracting More Than One Number ............................. | 39 | *2 pages* | 1 day | |
| Word Problems ......................................................... | 41 | *2 pages* | 1 day | |
| Chapter 5 Mixed Review ............................................ | 43 | *2 pages* | 1 day | |
| Chapter 5 Review ...................................................... | 45 | *2 pages* | 1 day | |
| Chapter 5 Test (optional) | | | | |
| **TOTALS** | | *30 pages* | 15 days | |

# Games and Activities

**10 Out** (or *6 Out, 7 Out, 8 Out, etc.*)

**You need:** A deck of number cards with numbers 1-10, or regular playing cards without the face cards.

**Preparation:** Choose a target sum, such as 10. Deal seven cards to each player. Place the rest face down in a pile in the middle of the table.

**Game play:** On your turn, first take one card from the pile. Then try to find pairs of cards in your hand that add up to 10, and discard any such pairs. Discard the card 10 also if you have it. If you cannot find any such pairs, ask for any one card you want (such as 6) from the player to your right (as in "Go Fish"). That player, if he has it, must give it, and you will then discard the pair that makes 10. Then it is the next player's turn. The player who first discards all the cards from his hand is the winner.

**Variations:**
* Deal more than seven cards.
* Deal fewer cards if there are a lot of players or the players are very young.
* Allow players to discard *three* cards that add up to 10.
* Instead of ten, players discard cards that add up to 5, 6, 7, 8, or 9.

### Rabbit Race

**You need:** A set of number cards from 1-10 OR a regular dice OR a 10-sided dice. A marker for each player. Download the game board from here:
https://www.mathmammoth.com/download/Rabbit-Race.pdf

**Game Play:** First, choose a number to subtract from, such as 10. This number can be any from 6 to 10. If you use 6, 7, 8, or 9 as this number, adjust your deck of number cards accordingly or use the regular dice (not the 10-sided dice). We don't want to end up with negative numbers!

On your turn, take a card from the deck or roll the dice. Subtract the number you get from 10. Then move your marker that many steps. Follow the instructions on the game board for any special squares. The winner is the player who first reaches the END.

### Addition (or Subtraction) Challenge

**You need:** A standard deck of playing cards from which you remove the face cards. For the addition version, you might also remove some of the other higher cards, such as tens, nines, and eights.

**Game Play:** In each round, each player is dealt two cards face up, and has to calculate their sum or difference (add/subtract). The player with the highest sum or difference gets all the cards from the other players. After enough rounds have been played to use all of the cards, the player with the most cards wins. If two or more players have the same sum, then those players get an additional two cards and use those to resolve the tie.

### Number Bonds in the Pond

**You need:** A standard deck (or several) of playing cards or number cards

**Preparation:** Choose a target sum for the game. If the target sum is 5, make a deck of cards consisting of numbers 1 through 4. If the target sum is 6, make a deck of numbers 1-5. And so on. (The deck always consists of numbers that are from 1 through $X - 1$ where $X$ is the target sum.) Place a target number card face up between the players, and spread out the rest of the cards face down, like a pond, between the players.

**Game play:** On your turn, if you don't have any cards in your hand, take <u>two</u> cards from the pond. If you do, take <u>one</u> card from the pond. Now check if any two cards in your hand add up to the target number. If so, put those cards away in your personal pile. If not, it is the next player's turn. The game ends when there are no more cards in the pond. The winner is the person with most cards in their personal pile.

**Variation:** Allow three cards/numbers to be added to reach the target number.

**Notes:** Depending on the number of players, you may need several decks of cards to make the pond. Playing this game several times will help the child to memorize the number bonds associated with a particular target number.

## Games and Activities at Math Mammoth Practice Zone

### Fact Families
Choose which fact family or families to practice, and the program will give you addition and subtraction problems from those, including with missing numbers.
https://www.mathmammoth.com/practice/fact-families

### Subtraction Hidden Picture Game
Choose a number range (such as 1 to 10) and uncover a hidden picture while solving subtraction problems!
https://www.mathmammoth.com/practice/mystery-picture-subtraction

### Number Bonds
Practice number bonds, either with pictures or with numbers.
https://www.mathmammoth.com/practice/number-bonds

### "7 Up" Card Game
You will see seven cards dealt face up. Simply choose any two cards that make 10 (or your chosen sum) to discard. When there are no cards that make that sum, click the deck to deal more cards. For this chapter, choose sums of 7, 8, 9, or 10.
https://www.mathmammoth.com/practice/seven-up

### Fruity Math
Add two single-digit numbers (such as 4 + 5). Click the fruit with the correct answer and try to get as many points as you can within two minutes.
https://www.mathmammoth.com/practice/fruity-math#o=a&d=120&m=m&c=2,5x1__1,7x1&s=120

### Bingo
Choose Subtraction (Under 10).
https://www.mathmammoth.com/practice/bingo

### Make Subtraction Sentences
You are given numbers (in flowers), and an answer to a subtraction. Drag two flowers to the empty slots so that the subtraction is true.
https://www.mathmammoth.com/practice/number-sentences#questions=5&types=sub-1-12

## Further Resources on the Internet

We have compiled a list of Internet resources that match the topics in this chapter, including pages that offer:

- **online practice** for concepts;
- online **games**, or occasionally, printable games;
- **animations** and interactive **illustrations** of math concepts;
- **articles** that teach a math concept.

We heartily recommend you take a look! Many of our customers love using these resources to supplement the bookwork. You can use these resources as you see fit for extra practice, to illustrate a concept better and even just for some fun. Enjoy!

## https://l.mathmammoth.com/2026/gr1ch5

Scan me

# Addition and Subtraction Facts with 4 and 5

Below you see the three different ways to group four buffalos into two groups. From the groupings we can write **three different fact families** where the **sum is** 4.

4 + 0 = 4          4 − 4 = 0

0 + 4 = 4          4 − 0 = 4

1 + 3 = 4          4 − 3 = 1

3 + 1 = 4          4 − 1 = 3

2 + 2 = 4          4 − 2 = 2

Similarly, we show below all the different ways to group *five* buffalos into two groups. From the groupings we get the **different fact families** where the **sum is** 5.

Fill in the missing parts.

5 + 0 = 5          5 − 5 = 0

____ + ____ = 5          5 − ____ = ____

4 + 1 = 5          5 − 4 = ____

1 + 4 = 5          5 − ____ = ____

3 + 2 = 5          5 − 3 = ____

____ + ____ = 5          5 − ____ = ____

You have probably already memorized all these addition and subtraction facts!

17

1. Fill in the missing numbers.

| a. | b. | c. | d. |
|---|---|---|---|
| 3 + _____ = 4 | 2 + _____ = 5 | 5 – 4 = _____ | 4 – 0 = _____ |
| 3 + _____ = 5 | 1 + _____ = 5 | 5 – 2 = _____ | 4 – 3 = _____ |
| 2 + _____ = 4 | 4 + _____ = 5 | 4 – 1 = _____ | 5 – 1 = _____ |

2. Color the square:

- yellow if the answer is 0,
- red if the answer is 1,
- blue if the answer is 2,
- green if the answer is 3,
- purple if the answer is 4,
- orange if the answer is 5.

| 5 – 4 | 2 + 3 | 4 – 4 | 1 + 2 | 4 – 2 | 1 + 3 |
|---|---|---|---|---|---|
| 2 + 2 | 3 – 2 | 5 – 0 | 0 + 0 | 5 – 2 | 1 + 1 |
| 0 + 2 | 5 – 1 | 0 + 1 | 1 + 4 | 0 – 0 | 4 – 1 |

3. Continue the patterns until the boxes are full!

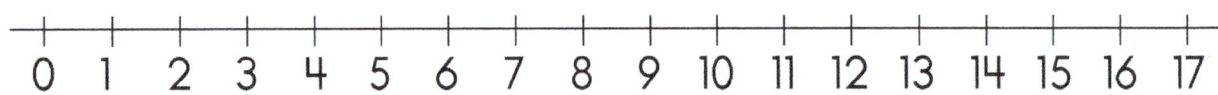

0  1  2  3  4  5  6  7  8  9  10  11  12  13  14  15  16  17

| a. | b. | c. |
|---|---|---|
| 17 – 0 = _____ | 10 + _____ = 10 | 5 – 2 = _____ |
| 17 – 1 = _____ | 10 + _____ = 11 | 6 – 2 = _____ |
| 17 – 2 = _____ | 10 + _____ = 12 | 7 – 2 = _____ |
| 17 – _____ = _____ | | |

# Addition and Subtraction Facts with 6

1. Complete the fact families in which the sum is six. At the top, write the three numbers that you are using for the fact family.

| 6, 0, 6 | _____, _____, 6 | _____, _____, 6 |
|---|---|---|

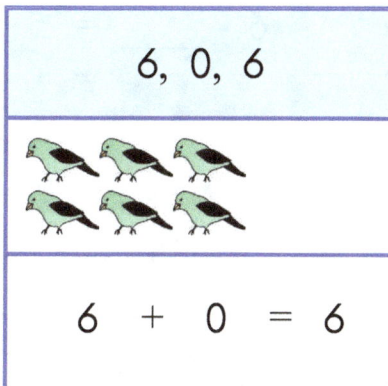

$6 + 0 = 6$

____ + ____ = 6

$6 - 6 = 0$

$6 - 0 = 6$

$5 + 1 = 6$

____ + ____ = 6

$6 - 5 = $ ____

$6 - $ ____ $= $ ____

$4 + 2 = 6$

____ + ____ = 6

$6 - 4 = $ ____

$6 - $ ____ $= $ ____

_____, _____, 6

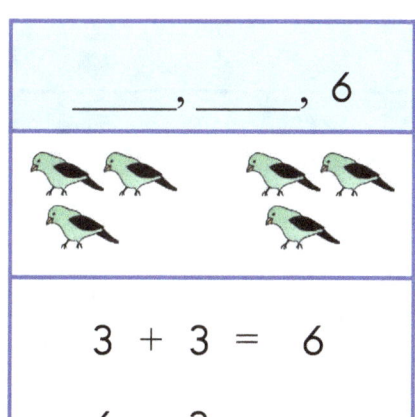

$3 + 3 = 6$

$6 - 3 = $ ____

2. Write the numbers that add to 6. Memorize these!

$0 + $ _____ $= 6$  or  _____ $+ 0 = 6$

$1 + $ _____ $= 6$  or  _____ $+ 1 = 6$

$2 + $ _____ $= 6$  or  _____ $+ 2 = 6$

$3 + $ _____ $= 6$

3. Play the "6 Out" card game (see the chapter introduction).

4. Subtract.

a.  $\begin{array}{r} 6 \\ -5 \\ \hline \end{array}$   b.  $\begin{array}{r} 6 \\ -4 \\ \hline \end{array}$   c.  $\begin{array}{r} 6 \\ -6 \\ \hline \end{array}$   d.  $\begin{array}{r} 6 \\ -2 \\ \hline \end{array}$   e.  $\begin{array}{r} 6 \\ -1 \\ \hline \end{array}$   f.  $\begin{array}{r} 6 \\ -3 \\ \hline \end{array}$

5. Fill in the missing numbers.

| a. | b. | c. | d. |
|---|---|---|---|
| 4 + _____ = 6 | 5 + _____ = 6 | _____ + 2 = 6 | 6 − _____ = 2 |
| 3 + _____ = 6 | 0 + _____ = 6 | _____ + 1 = 6 | 6 − _____ = 5 |

6. Mike counted his toy cars. He has three yellow
   ones, four blue ones, and three red ones.
   How many toy cars does he have in all?

7. For each "how many more" addition, write a subtraction using the same numbers so
   that the numbers in the hexagons are the same.

a.  2 + ⬡ = 5

   5 − 2 = ⬡3

b.  1 + ⬡ = 6

   _____ − _____ = ⬡

c.  4 + ⬡ = 5

   _____ − _____ = ⬡

d.  3 + ⬡ = 6

   _____ − _____ = ⬡

e.  5 + ⬡ = 10

   _____ − _____ = ⬡

f.  2 + ⬡ = 6

   _____ − _____ = ⬡

**Puzzle Corner**  Find the number that goes in place of the shape.

a. 40 + ⬡ + 20 + 30 = 100

b. 5 + ▲ + 4 + 7 = 20

# Word Problems and Symbols

What number fits in place of the dot?

Five, because $8 - 5$ equals 3.

So, the dot equals 5. We write that under the equation.

$$8 - \bullet = 3$$

$$\bullet = \underline{\phantom{0}5\phantom{0}}$$

1. Find the number that the shape stands for. Write it on the line below the problem.

| a. | b. | c. | d. |
|---|---|---|---|
| $4 - \bullet = 3$ | $2 + \bullet = 7$ | $\bullet - 3 = 1$ | $\bullet + 6 = 9$ |
| $\bullet = \underline{\phantom{0000}}$ | $\bullet = \underline{\phantom{0000}}$ | $\bullet = \underline{\phantom{0000}}$ | $\bullet = \underline{\phantom{0000}}$ |
| e. | f. | g. | h. |
| $6 = 2 + \bullet$ | $5 = 1 + \bullet$ | $5 = \bullet - 1$ | $4 = 6 - \bullet$ |
| $\bullet = \underline{\phantom{0000}}$ | $\bullet = \underline{\phantom{0000}}$ | $\bullet = \underline{\phantom{0000}}$ | $\bullet = \underline{\phantom{0000}}$ |

2. Solve the problems. Think: Are you asked for the total? Are you asked how many more? Or are you asked how many are left?

**a.** Mother has clothespins in two containers: a red one and a blue one. The red container has 10 clothespins. The blue one has two fewer clothespins than the red one. How many clothespins are in the blue container?


How many clothespins are there in total?


**b.** John lost two of his crayons, and now he has six left. How many crayons did he have at first?

3. Fill in the missing numbers.

a. $0 + \underline{\quad} = 6$

$3 + \underline{\quad} = 6$

$5 + \underline{\quad} = 6$

b. $5 = 3 + \underline{\quad}$

$5 = 5 + \underline{\quad}$

$5 = 4 + \underline{\quad}$

c. $5 - \underline{\quad} = 2$

$6 - \underline{\quad} = 4$

$5 - \underline{\quad} = 1$

4. Solve.

a. The black cat has four kittens and the white cat has three.
How many kittens do they have altogether?

How many more kittens does the black cat have
than the white cat?

b. Seven birds sat in a tree. One of them was black,
two were blue, and the rest were brown.
How many were brown?

c. Ella had some red, some blue, and some yellow
roses in a vase. Two of the roses were blue, and
two were red. If she had a total of ten roses,
how many of them were yellow?

d. (challenge) Ivy has two eggs. She needs eight eggs to make some cakes.
If her neighbor gives Ivy three eggs, will she have enough?

If not, how many more does she still need?

# Addition and Subtraction Facts with 7

1. Complete the fact families with 7. At the top, write the three numbers you are using.

| 7, 0, 7 | ____, ____, 7 | ____, ____, 7 |
|---|---|---|

7 + 0 = 7

____ + ____ = 7

7 – ____ = ____

7 – ____ = ____


6 + ____ = 7

____ + ____ = 7

7 – ____ = ____

____ – ____ = ____


5 + ____ = 7

____ + ____ = 7

7 – ____ = ____

____ – ____ = ____


____, ____, 7

4 + ____ = 7

____ + ____ = 7

7 – ____ = ____

____ – ____ = ____

2. Write down the numbers that add up to 7 and memorize the addition facts!

0 + ____ = 7    or    ____ + 0 = 7

1 + ____ = 7    or    ____ + 1 = 7

2 + ____ = 7    or    ____ + 2 = 7

3 + ____ = 7    or    ____ + 3 = 7

3. Play the "7 Out" card game (see the chapter introduction).

4. Subtract.

a.  7   b.  7   c.  7   d.  7   e.  7   f.  7
  − 5     − 4     − 6     − 2     − 1     − 3

5. Solve.

a. Luis has four pencils. Jeremy has two more than Luis.
   How many pencils does Jeremy have?



   How many pencils do the two boys have altogether?

b. Maria found two socks in the hamper, five socks in her basket,
   and one sock on the floor. How many socks did she find?

6. Fill in. Then draw a line between the facts that are from the same fact family.

5 + _____ = 7        7 − _____ = 4        7 − 1 = 6

7 − 0 = _____        6 + 1 = 7            _____ + 4 = 7

7 − 3 = _____        7 − 2 = _____        7 − _____ = 7

7 − 6 = 1            0 + _____ = 7        7 − _____ = 2

**Puzzle Corner**  Figure out how to fill in the rest of this subtraction table.

| − | 12 | 11 | 10 | 9 | 8 | 7 | 6 | 5 | 4 | 3 |
|---|----|----|----|---|---|---|---|---|---|---|
| 1 | 11 |    |    |   |   | 6 |   |   |   |   |
| 2 |    | 9  |    |   |   |   | 4 |   |   | 1 |

24

# Addition and Subtraction Facts with 8

1. Complete the fact families in which the sum is eight.

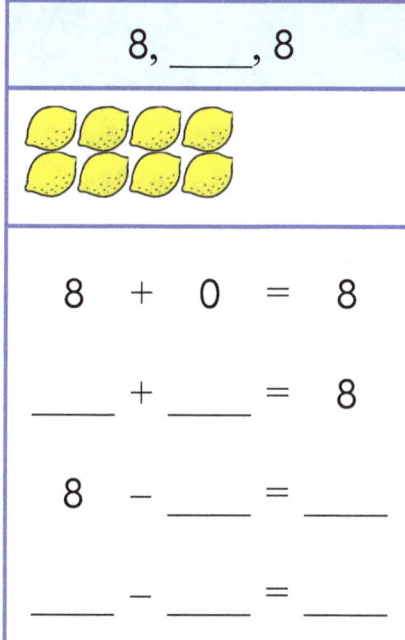

8, _____, 8

8 + 0 = 8

_____ + _____ = 8

8 − _____ = _____

_____ − _____ = _____

_____, _____, 8

7 + 1 = 8

_____ + _____ = 8

8 − _____ = _____

_____ − _____ = _____

_____, _____, 8

_____ + _____ = _____

_____ + _____ = _____

_____ − _____ = _____

_____ − _____ = _____

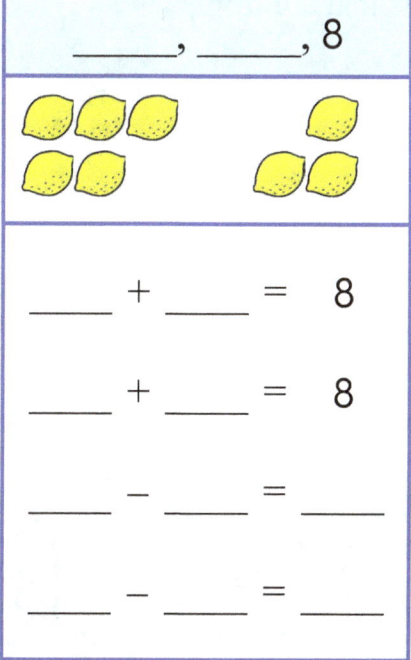

_____, _____, 8

_____ + _____ = 8

_____ + _____ = 8

_____ − _____ = _____

_____ − _____ = _____

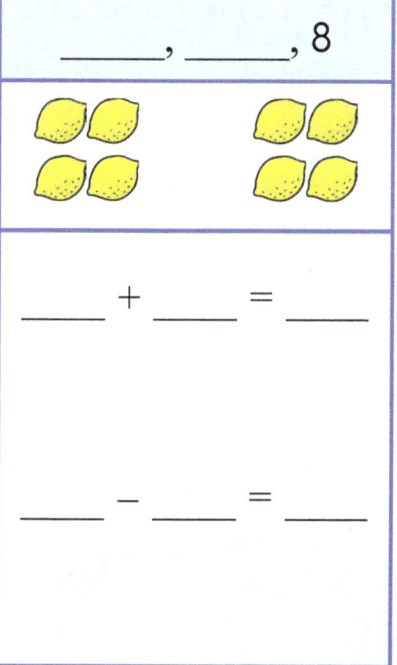

_____, _____, 8

_____ + _____ = _____

_____ − _____ = _____

2. Play the "8 Out" card game (see the chapter introduction).

3. Write the addition facts with 8 and memorize them!

$0 + \underline{\hspace{1cm}} = 8$   or   $\underline{\hspace{1cm}} + 0 = 8$

$1 + \underline{\hspace{1cm}} = 8$   or   $\underline{\hspace{1cm}} + 1 = 8$

$2 + \underline{\hspace{1cm}} = 8$   or   $\underline{\hspace{1cm}} + \underline{\hspace{1cm}} = 8$

$3 + \underline{\hspace{1cm}} = 8$   or   $\underline{\hspace{1cm}} + \underline{\hspace{1cm}} = 8$

$4 + \underline{\hspace{1cm}} = 8$

4. Circle all the *true* equations.

a.   $50 = 70 - 20$         b.   $0 = 0$         c.   $2 + 6 = 9$

d.   $10 = 100 - 80$       e.   $11 = 13$       f.   $7 - 3 = 5$

g.   $2 + 7 = 9$             h.   $9 = 5 + 3$     i.   $54 - 10 = 45$

5. Fill in the missing numbers and draw a line between the facts that are from the same fact family.

$6 + \underline{2} = 8$

$8 - 0 = \underline{\hspace{1cm}}$

$8 - 3 = \underline{\hspace{1cm}}$

$\underline{\hspace{1cm}} + 1 = 8$

$4 + \underline{\hspace{1cm}} = 8$

---

$8 - 4 = \underline{\hspace{1cm}}$

$8 - \underline{\hspace{1cm}} = 3$

$7 + \underline{\hspace{1cm}} = 8$

$8 - 2 = \underline{6}$

$0 + \underline{\hspace{1cm}} = 8$

---

$\underline{\hspace{1cm}} + 5 = 8$

$8 - \underline{2} = 6$

$\underline{\hspace{1cm}} + 4 = 8$

$8 - \underline{\hspace{1cm}} = 8$

$8 - 1 = \underline{\hspace{1cm}}$

**Puzzle Corner**

Solve.

a.   $20 - \underline{\hspace{1cm}} = 11 + 2$       b.   $\underline{\hspace{1cm}} - 10 = 7 + 8$

c.   $16 - 2 = \underline{\hspace{1cm}} - 7$         d.   $53 - 2 = 60 - \underline{\hspace{1cm}}$

# Review — Facts with 6, 7, and 8

1. Practice addition and subtraction facts with 6, 7, and 8.

**a.**

$0 + \underline{\hspace{1cm}} = 8$

$3 + \underline{\hspace{1cm}} = 8$

$2 + \underline{\hspace{1cm}} = 8$

$6 + \underline{\hspace{1cm}} = 8$

$5 + \underline{\hspace{1cm}} = 8$

**b.**

$3 + \underline{\hspace{1cm}} = 7$

$5 + \underline{\hspace{1cm}} = 7$

$1 + \underline{\hspace{1cm}} = 7$

$6 + \underline{\hspace{1cm}} = 7$

$2 + \underline{\hspace{1cm}} = 7$

**c.**

$6 - \underline{\hspace{1cm}} = 2$

$6 - \underline{\hspace{1cm}} = 5$

$6 - \underline{\hspace{1cm}} = 3$

$6 - \underline{\hspace{1cm}} = 4$

$6 - \underline{\hspace{1cm}} = 1$

**d.**

$7 - \underline{\hspace{1cm}} = 2$

$8 - \underline{\hspace{1cm}} = 3$

$6 - \underline{\hspace{1cm}} = 1$

$8 - \underline{\hspace{1cm}} = 4$

$7 - \underline{\hspace{1cm}} = 4$

2. First add and subtract. Then compare, writing <, >, or = in the box.

**a.** $8 - 2$ ❓ $7 - 3$

$\downarrow$ ☐ $\downarrow$

**b.** $10 - 7$ ❓ $9 - 6$

$\downarrow$ ☐ $\downarrow$

**c.** $7 - 6$ ❓ $4 - 2$

$\downarrow$ ☐ $\downarrow$

**d.** $4 + 2$ ☐ $9 - 8$

**e.** $10 - 4$ ☐ $7 - 4$

**f.** $3 + 4$ ☐ $7 - 1$

3. Solve.

**a.** Luisa and Caleb were playing a game.
Caleb had 4 game pieces. Luisa had 5 more than Caleb.
How many game pieces did Luisa have?

**b.** Luisa gave one game piece to Caleb.
Now who has more game pieces?

How many more?

4. Complete. Then draw lines to connect the facts from the same fact family.

_____ − 5 = 1

2 + _____ = 7

8 − _____ = 3

_____ + 2 = 8

6 − 4 = _____

7 − 5 = _____

_____ + 2 = 6

6 − 1 = _____

5 + _____ = 8

8 − _____ = 6

8 − 3 = _____

5 + _____ = 7

1 + 5 = _____

8 − 6 = _____

2 + 4 = _____

5. Complete. Then draw lines to connect the facts from the same fact family.

3 + _____ = 7

6 − _____ = 3

_____ + 1 = 8

_____ − 4 = 4

7 − 1 = _____

_____ + 6 = 7

_____ − 7 = 1

3 + 3 = _____

4 + _____ = 7

8 − _____ = 4

8 − _____ = 7

1 + 6 = _____

3 + _____ = 6

8 − 4 = _____

7 − _____ = 4

Puzzle Corner

What numbers can go into the puzzles? Guess and check!

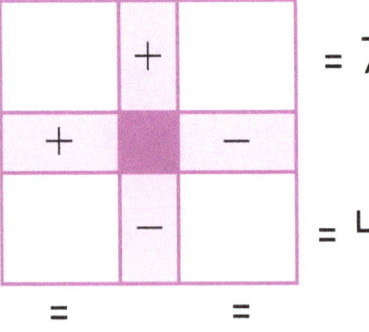

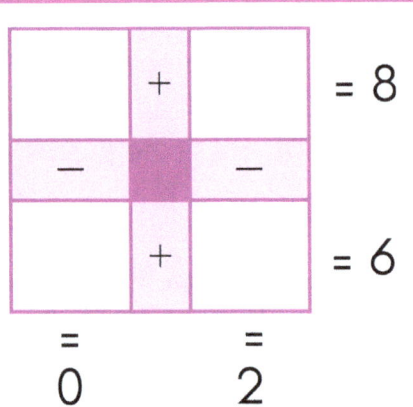

# Comparisons and Word Problems

First calculate. Write the answer(s) below. Then compare.

| Example 1. | $6 - 2$ | ? | 5 | Example 2. | $4 + 2$ | ? | $8 - 3$ |
|---|---|---|---|---|---|---|---|
| | ↓ | | ↓ | | ↓ | | ↓ |
| | 4 | $<$ | 5 | | 6 | $>$ | 5 |

1. First subtract. Write the answer in the shaded box below. Then compare.

**a.** $7 - 4$ ? 5
↓     ↓
☐ 5

**b.** $8 - 1$ ? 7
↓     ↓
☐

**c.** 2 ? $6 - 3$
↓     ↓
☐

2. First add and subtract. Then compare, and write $<$, $>$ or $=$.

**a.** $5 - 2$ ? $4 - 2$
↓     ↓
☐

**b.** $8 - 1$ ? $7 - 1$
↓     ↓
☐

**c.** $8 - 6$ ? $8 - 5$
↓     ↓
☐

**d.** $6 + 2$ ? $7 + 2$
↓     ↓
☐

**e.** $7 - 2$ ? $6 - 1$
↓     ↓
☐

**f.** $4 + 4$ ? $7 - 5$
↓     ↓
☐

**g.** $1 - 1$ ? $3 - 2$
↓     ↓
☐

**h.** $3 + 10$ ? 10
↓     ↓
☐

**i.** 7 ? $4 + 2$
↓     ↓
☐

3. Fill in the missing numbers.

| a. | b. | c. | d. |
|---|---|---|---|
| 8 − 3 = _____ | 5 + _____ = 7 | 8 = 4 + _____ | 7 − 2 = _____ |
| 8 − 6 = _____ | 1 + _____ = 7 | 8 = 6 + _____ | 7 − 0 = _____ |
| 8 − 4 = _____ | 2 + _____ = 7 | 8 = 1 + _____ | 7 − 4 = _____ |

4. Which equation matches the situation?

Ashley has five pencils in her backpack, some short, and some long ones. Two are short. How many are long?

$5 + 2 = 7$

$5 − 2 = 3$

$5 = 2 + 3$

5. Solve the word problems. Drawing or acting it out can help you.

**a.** Jack has 10 cars, Bill has 7, and Ed has 4.

How many more cars does Bill have than Ed?

How many more cars does Jack have than Ed ?

**b.** Eight bees were visiting the flowers of a tree. Then five of them flew to another tree. How many are now in the first tree?

**c.** Four sheep were eating grass in a pasture. The farmer brought three other sheep to join them. Later, he brought two more sheep. How many sheep are there now?

# Addition and Subtraction Facts with 9

1. Write the fact families where the sum is 9.

| 9, 0, 9 |  _____, _____, 9 |  _____, _____, 9 |
|---|---|---|

9 + ____ = 9

____ + ____ = 9

9 − ____ = ____

_____ − ____ = _____

_____ + _____ = _____

_____ + _____ = _____

_____ − _____ = _____

_____ − _____ = _____

_____ + _____ = _____

_____ + _____ = _____

_____ − _____ = _____

_____ − _____ = _____

 _____, _____, 9

 _____, _____, 9

_____ + _____ = _____

_____ + _____ = _____

_____ − _____ = _____

_____ − _____ = _____

_____ + _____ = _____

_____ + _____ = _____

_____ − _____ = _____

_____ − _____ = _____

2. Play the "9 Out" card game (see chapter introduction).

31

3. Write the addition
facts with 9 and
memorize them!

$0 +$ _____ $= 9$    or    _____ $+ \; 0 \; = 9$

$1 +$ _____ $= 9$    or    _____ $+ \; 1 \; = 9$

$2 +$ _____ $= 9$    or    _____ $+$ _____ $= 9$

$3 +$ _____ $= 9$    or    _____ $+$ _____ $= 9$

$4 +$ _____ $= 9$    or    _____ $+$ _____ $= 9$

4. Find the number that the shape stands for.

| a. | b. | c. | d. |
|---|---|---|---|
| $10 - \triangle = 2$ | $9 = 3 + \triangle$ | $6 = \triangle - 3$ | $\triangle - 4 = 5$ |
| $\triangle =$ _____ | $\triangle =$ _____ | $\triangle =$ _____ | $\triangle =$ _____ |

5. Fill in the missing numbers.

| a. | b. | c. | d. |
|---|---|---|---|
| $9 - 5 =$ _____ | $2 +$ _____ $= 9$ | _____ $+ 1 = 9$ | $9 -$ _____ $= 1$ |
| $9 - 3 =$ _____ | $1 +$ _____ $= 9$ | _____ $+ 3 = 9$ | $9 -$ _____ $= 0$ |
| $9 - 6 =$ _____ | $7 +$ _____ $= 9$ | _____ $+ 5 = 9$ | $9 -$ _____ $= 2$ |
| $9 - 8 =$ _____ | $8 +$ _____ $= 9$ | _____ $+ 7 = 9$ | $9 -$ _____ $= 4$ |

6. First add or subtract in your head. Then compare and write $<$ , $>$ or $=$ in the box.

a.    $8 \ \square \ 10 - 3$    b.    $9 \ \square \ 9 + 3$    c. $8 - 6 \ \square \ 6 + 3$

d. $6 + 2 \ \square \ 8 + 2$    e. $10 - 1 \ \square \ 10$    f. $8 - 4 \ \square \ 8 - 5$

# More Practice

1. Fill in. Then draw lines to connect the facts that belong to the same fact family.

| | | |
|---|---|---|
| 7 + _____ = 9 | 0 + _____ = 9 | _____ + 8 = 9 |
| 9 − 3 = _____ | 9 − _____ = 3 | 9 − _____ = 6 |
| 9 − 1 = _____ | 5 + _____ = 9 | _____ + 2 = 9 |
| 9 − _____ = 9 | 9 − 2 = _____ | 9 − _____ = 4 |
| 4 + _____ = 9 | 9 − _____ = 1 | _____ + 0 = 9 |

2. Compare, and write < , > or = in the box.

a. $5 - 2$ ☐ $4 - 2$      b. $8$ ☐ $8 - 0$      c. $9 - 6$ ☐ $2 + 2$

3. Continue the patterns.

a.
$9 - 1 =$ _____

$9 - 2 =$ _____

$9 - 3 =$ _____

_____ − _____ = _____

_____ − _____ = _____

_____ − _____ = _____

_____ − _____ = _____

b.
$0 +$ _____ $= 10$

$1 +$ _____ $= 10$

$2 +$ _____ $= 10$

_____ + _____ = _____

_____ + _____ = _____

_____ + _____ = _____

_____ + _____ = _____

4. Subtract.

a.  $\begin{array}{r} 9 \\ -5 \\ \hline \end{array}$  b.  $\begin{array}{r} 9 \\ -4 \\ \hline \end{array}$  c.  $\begin{array}{r} 9 \\ -6 \\ \hline \end{array}$  d.  $\begin{array}{r} 8 \\ -2 \\ \hline \end{array}$  e.  $\begin{array}{r} 9 \\ -2 \\ \hline \end{array}$  f.  $\begin{array}{r} 8 \\ -3 \\ \hline \end{array}$

5. Which equations match the word problem? (It could be one or two.) Solve.

| **a.** Millie has two stuffed bears. Ken has seven. How many more bears does Ken have? | $2 + \underline{\hspace{1cm}} = 7$ <br><br> $7 + 2 = \underline{\hspace{1cm}}$ <br><br> $2 = \underline{\hspace{1cm}} + 7$ |
|---|---|
| **b.** Elisa knows she has ten crayons. She can only find four. How many are missing? | $4 + 10 = \underline{\hspace{1cm}}$ <br><br> $10 - 4 = \underline{\hspace{1cm}}$ <br><br> $4 + \underline{\hspace{1cm}} = 10$ |

6. If the answer is 6 or 7, color its box blue. If the answer is 8 or 9, color its box red, and color the rest of the boxes yellow.

| $9 - 3$ | $4 + 6$ | $9 - 0$ | $4 + 6$ | $8 - 1$ |
|---|---|---|---|---|
| $2 + 5$ | $9 - 5$ | $4 + 4$ | $4 - 2$ | $5 + 1$ |
| $9 - 2$ | $3 + 7$ | $10 - 2$ | $10 + 0$ | $7 - 1$ |
| $4 + 2$ | $7 - 3$ | $6 + 3$ | $3 - 1$ | $3 + 3$ |
| $6 - 0$ | $1 + 1$ | $8 - 0$ | $3 + 2$ | $10 - 4$ |
| $3 + 4$ | $8 - 3$ | $2 + 7$ | $7 - 6$ | $7 + 0$ |
| $1 + 6$ | $2 + 8$ | $10 - 1$ | $2 + 2$ | $7 - 0$ |

# Addition and Subtraction Facts with 10

1. Complete the fact families in which the sum is ten.

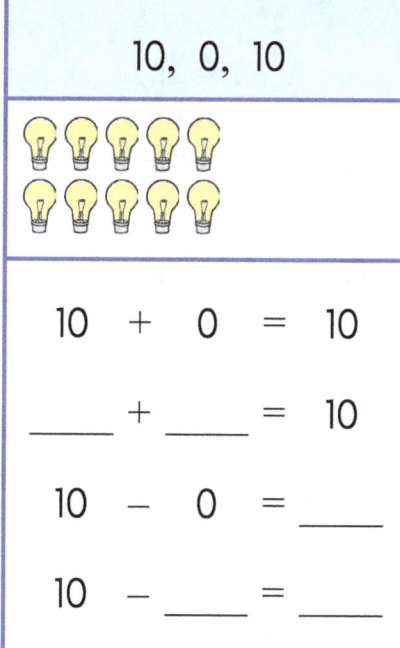

10, 0, 10

10 + 0 = 10

____ + ____ = 10

10 − 0 = ____

10 − ____ = ____

9, 1, 10

9 + ____ = 10

____ + ____ = 10

10 − 9 = ____

10 − ____ = ____

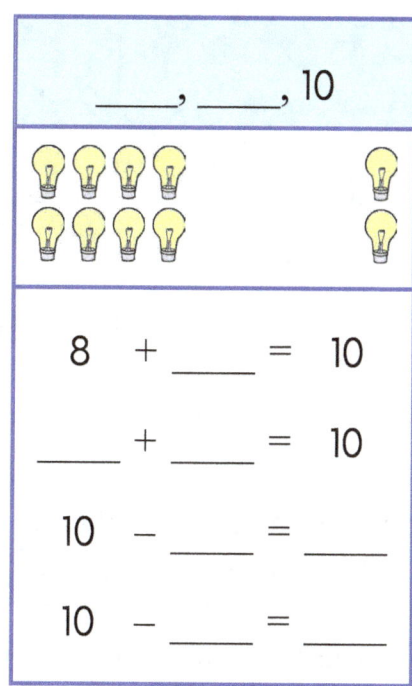

____, ____, 10

8 + ____ = 10

____ + ____ = 10

10 − ____ = ____

10 − ____ = ____

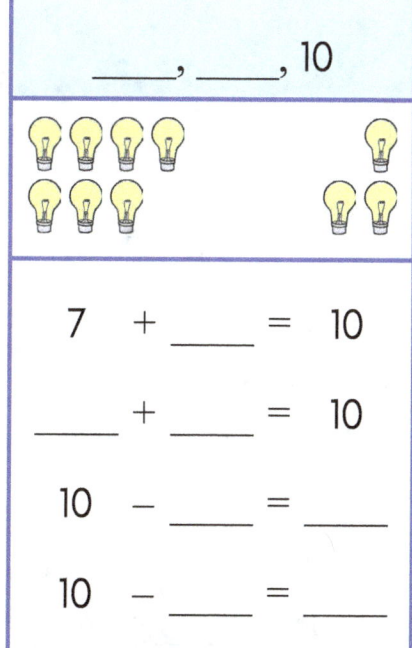

____, ____, 10

7 + ____ = 10

____ + ____ = 10

10 − ____ = ____

10 − ____ = ____

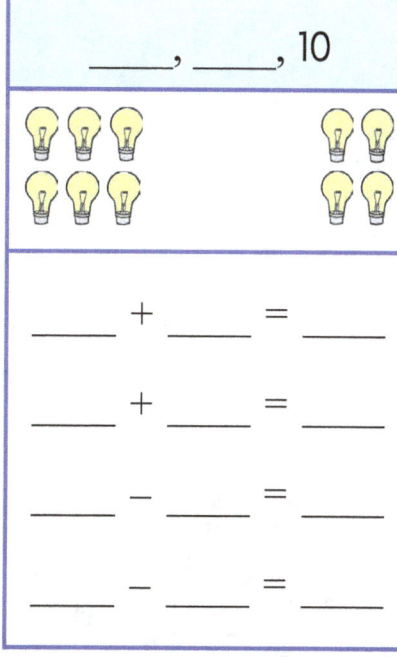

____, ____, 10

____ + ____ = ____

____ + ____ = ____

____ − ____ = ____

____ − ____ = ____

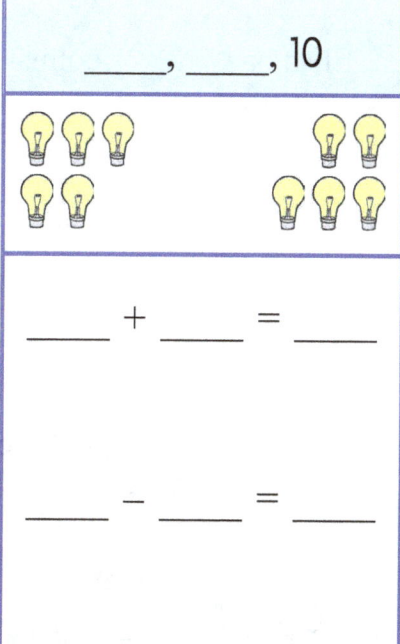

____, ____, 10

____ + ____ = ____

____ + ____ = ____

____ − ____ = ____

____ − ____ = ____

2. Play the "10 Out" card game (see the chapter introduction).

3. Write the addition facts with 10 and memorize them!

0 + _____ = 10     or     _____ + 0 = 10

1 + _____ = 10     or     _____ + 1 = 10

2 + _____ = 10     or     _____ + _____ = 10

3 + _____ = 10     or     _____ + _____ = 10

4 + _____ = 10     or     _____ + _____ = 10

5 + _____ = 10

4. Solve. Write an addition or a subtraction equation for each problem. Write either + or − symbol in the gray box.

**a.** Elisa has two coins in her piggy bank. Today Elisa found three coins on the ground. How many coins does Elisa have now?

_____ ☐ _____ = _____

Elisa has _____ coins now.

**b.** Sarah has six coins in her piggy bank and Alfonso has eight. How many more coins does Alfonso have than Sarah?

_____ ☐ _____ = _____

Alfonso has _____ more coins than Sarah.

5. Fill in the missing numbers.

| a. | b. | c. |
|---|---|---|
| 10 − 3 = _____ | 0 + _____ = 10 | 10 − _____ = 7 |
| 10 − 6 = _____ | 7 + _____ = 10 | 10 − _____ = 2 |
| 10 − 2 = _____ | 9 + _____ = 10 | 10 − _____ = 4 |

# Review of Facts with 9 and 10

1. Practice addition and subtraction facts with 9 and 10.

| a. | b. | c. | d. |
|---|---|---|---|
| $9 = 4 + \underline{\hphantom{xx}}$ | $10 = 5 + \underline{\hphantom{xx}}$ | $10 - \underline{\hphantom{xx}} = 1$ | $9 - \underline{\hphantom{xx}} = 2$ |
| $9 = 1 + \underline{\hphantom{xx}}$ | $10 = 2 + \underline{\hphantom{xx}}$ | $10 - \underline{\hphantom{xx}} = 7$ | $9 - \underline{\hphantom{xx}} = 6$ |
| $9 = 6 + \underline{\hphantom{xx}}$ | $10 = 3 + \underline{\hphantom{xx}}$ | $10 - \underline{\hphantom{xx}} = 5$ | $9 - \underline{\hphantom{xx}} = 8$ |
| $9 = 2 + \underline{\hphantom{xx}}$ | $10 = 4 + \underline{\hphantom{xx}}$ | $10 - \underline{\hphantom{xx}} = 8$ | $9 - \underline{\hphantom{xx}} = 5$ |

2. Solve. Remember, you can always draw a picture of the situation to help you!

Dad had one box of nails at home, and then he bought six more boxes of nails. The next day he gave one box to the neighbor.

How many boxes of nails does Dad have now?

3. a. Draw a line to connect each pair of numbers that add up to 9.
Which number is left by itself?

```
0        7      2
   2       8      5
1      6
  9        4   3   4
     5
  1           3   8
7         6         9
```

b. Draw a line to connect each pair of numbers that add up to 10.
Which number is left by itself?

```
3        7    10
   2       8      9
1      6
  9        4   0   2
     5
  1           3   8
7         6         5
```

1. Fill in. Then draw lines to connect the facts that are from the same fact family.

6 + _____ = 10

10 − 5 = _____

10 − 1 = _____

10 − 2 = _____

7 + _____ = 10

8 + _____ = 10

10 − _____ = 3

5 + _____ = 10

10 − 4 = _____

9 + _____ = 10

_____ + 5 = 10

10 − _____ = 6

_____ + 2 = 10

10 − _____ = 7

10 − 9 = _____

5. Write fact families so that the numbers in the hexagons are the same.

a.  1  +  ⬡  =  6

⬡  +  _____  =  _____

_____ − ⬡  =  _____

_____ − _____  =  ⬡

b.  2  +  7  =  ⬡

_____ + _____  =  ⬡

⬡ − _____  =  _____

⬡ − _____  =  _____

**Puzzle Corner** Each shape represents a number. Find what the numbers are.
**Hint:** You can simply guess and check, then improve your guess.

a.   + ▲ = 10

⬠ − ▲ = 2

⬠ is _____

▲ is _____

b.  ● + ⬡ = 10

● − ⬡ = 6

● is _____

⬡ is _____

c.  ◆ + ⬡ = 10

◆ − ⬡ = 0

◆ is _____

⬡ is _____

# Subtracting More Than One Number

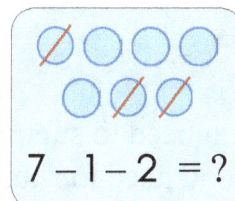

$7 - 1 - 2 = ?$

You have 7 circles. First you take away 1 circle, and then you take away 2 more circles.

You will have 4 circles left.

1. Subtract twice, taking away circles. You can cover circles to help.

| a. 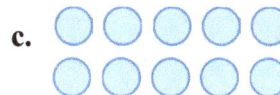 | b. | c. |
|---|---|---|
| $8 - 2 - 3 =$ _____ | $9 - 3 - 1 =$ _____ | $10 - 5 - 3 =$ _____ |
| $8 - 5 - 2 =$ _____ | $9 - 4 - 2 =$ _____ | $10 - 6 - 2 =$ _____ |
| $8 - 1 - 3 =$ _____ | $9 - 2 - 5 =$ _____ | $10 - 1 - 4 =$ _____ |

2. Solve.

**a.** Maria had ten cookies. She gave two to her brother and two to her sister. How many does she have left?

**b.** Seven birds were in the tree. Three flew away. After a while, one more flew away. How many birds were left in the tree?

**c.** Two cars were in the parking lot. Then three cars came in. After that two more cars came in. How many cars are there now?

**d.** Some boys were playing basketball. Then two more boys came in, and now there are seven boys playing. How many were there at first?

| You can subtract the first two numbers first: | OR you can subtract their total: |
|---|---|

You can subtract the first two numbers first:

$$8 - 2 - 3$$
$$\diagdown \diagup$$
$$6 \quad - 3 = 3$$

First take away 2. That leaves 6.
Then, from 6, subtract 3. That leaves 3.

OR you can subtract their total:

$$8 - 2 - 3$$
$$\diagdown \diagup$$
$$8 - 5 \quad = 3$$

Check how much you need to subtract or take away *in total*. You need to subtract 2 and 3 — a total of 5. So subtract 8 − 5 = 3.

3. Subtract by either method.

| a. | b. | c. |
|---|---|---|
| 7 − 2 − 3 = _____ | 9 − 7 − 1 = _____ | 7 − 5 − 1 = _____ |
| 9 − 2 − 6 = _____ | 6 − 2 − 2 = _____ | 10 − 6 − 1 = _____ |

4. Solve. Compare the two problems and their results.

| a. | b. | c. |
|---|---|---|
| 10 − 3 − 2 = _____ | 7 − 3 − 3 = _____ | 9 − 6 − 1 = _____ |
| 10 − 3 − 3 = _____ | 7 − 4 − 3 = _____ | 8 − 6 − 1 = _____ |

5. Match each subtraction problem to a correct picture.

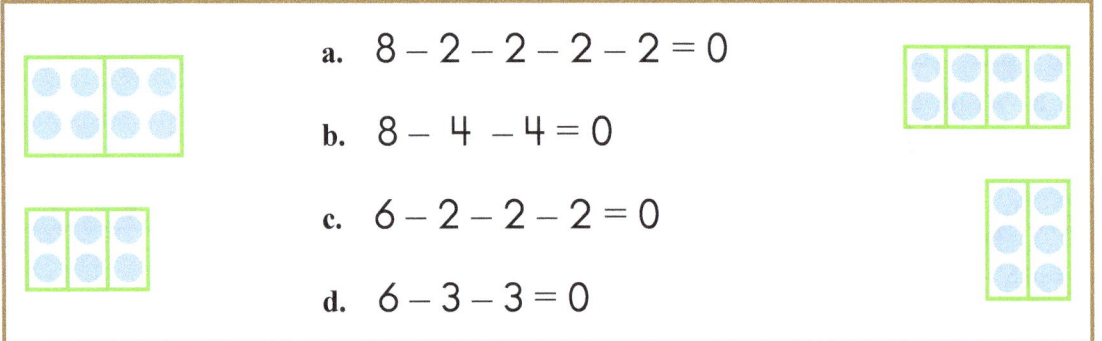

a. 8 − 2 − 2 − 2 − 2 = 0

b. 8 − 4 − 4 = 0

c. 6 − 2 − 2 − 2 = 0

d. 6 − 3 − 3 = 0

**Puzzle Corner** Here are some problems with four numbers!

9 − 3 − 2 − 1 = _____    10 − 1 − 2 − 1 = _____    8 − 4 − 1 − 2 = _____

# Word Problems

Be careful with problems that mention "more" or "fewer." It is always helpful to draw and check carefully that the drawing matches what the problem says.

*Ricardo and Olivia played a card game. In the end, Ricardo had three fewer cards than Olivia. Ricardo had five cards. How many did Olivia have?*

Which illustration matches the problem?

Ricardo ☐☐☐☐

Olivia ☐☐☐

or

Ricardo ☐☐☐☐

Olivia ☐☐☐☐☐☐☐

1. Solve the problems.

**a.** Ben has seven marbles. Kai has three fewer marbles than him.
How many does Kai have?

**b.** Sofia has two more toy horses than Evelyn. Sofia has 6 horses.
How many does Evelyn have?

**c.** Charlie and Mollie are dogs. Mollie ate three more eggs than Charlie. Mollie ate six eggs. How many did Charlie eat?

**d.** A big banana tree has 10 bananas on it.
A small tree has three fewer bananas than that.
How many does the small one have?

How many do the two trees have together?

2. Solve. Write an addition or a subtraction for each problem.
   (Write a + or − symbol in the box.)

**a.** A ten-piece puzzle has two pieces missing.
   How many pieces are there now?

   There are _____ pieces now.

   _____ ☐ _____ = _____

**b.** Mia saw three kittens with Mommy Cat.
   Then three more kittens came.
   How many kittens are there now?

   There are _____ kittens now.

   _____ ☐ _____ = _____

3. Which equation matches the question? Solve.

Mom put a bunch of strawberries on Tony's plate.
He ate 8 of them. Now he still has two left on his
plate. How many were on his plate at first?

$8 - \bigcirc = 2$

$8 - 2 = \bigcirc$

$\bigcirc - 8 = 2$

4. Solve.

**a.** A bunch of children were playing at the playground.
   Then four of them left. Now there are two children still
   playing. How many were there at first?

**b.** (challenge) Emilia is playing with four toy cars. She has two more cars than
   her brother Leo. And Leo has four fewer cars than his brother David.

   How many cars does David have?

   How many cars do the three children have in total?

# Chapter 5 Mixed Review

1. Draw an arrow to illustrate each subtraction, and solve.

a. $10 - 4 =$ _____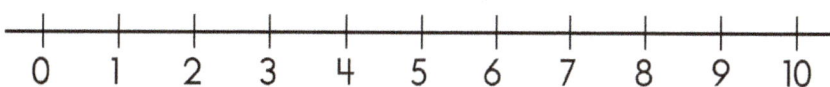

b. $8 - 5 =$ _____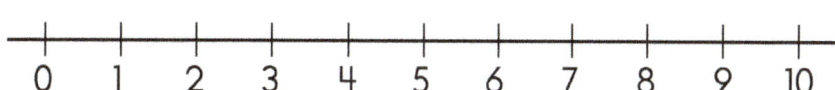

2. Circle.

a. The sixth car from the left.

b. The fourth car from the right.

c. The eighth heart from the right.

3. Add. You can color the numbers you want to add first!

| a. $2 + 1 + 5 =$ | b. $4 + 2 + 4 =$ | c. $3 + 1 + 3 =$ |
|---|---|---|
| d. $2 + 5 + 0 + 2 =$ | | e. $3 + 3 + 1 + 3 =$ |
| f. $4 + 1 + 1 + 2 =$ | | g. $1 + 1 + 2 + 2 =$ |

4. Find the difference between the numbers. "Travel" on the number line!

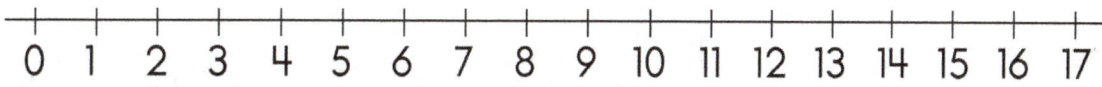

| | | | | | | | |
|---|---|---|---|---|---|---|---|
| From | 6 | 6 | 1 | 7 | 7 | 10 | 12 |
| To | 8 | 11 | 8 | 2 | 11 | 17 | 9 |
| Difference | | | | | | | |

5. Draw more dots to make both sides have the same number of dots. Fill in the missing numbers.

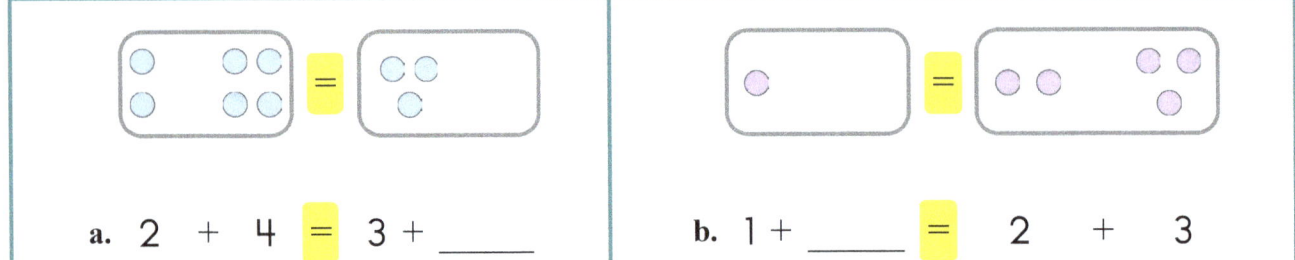

a. $2 + 4 = 3 +$ _____

b. $1 +$ _____ $= 2 + 3$

6. Fill in the missing numbers. You can draw dots to help you.

| | | |
|---|---|---|
| a. $5 =$ _____ $+ 1$ | b. $10 =$ _____ $+ 5$ | c. $9 =$ _____ $+ 2$ |
| d. _____ $= 4 + 3$ | e. _____ $= 9 + 1$ | f. _____ $= 4 + 5$ |

7. Which of the given numbers fits the comparison below? Write it on the empty line.

| a. 73    80    68 | b. 39    51    46 | c. 59    102    92 |
|---|---|---|
| 72 > _____ | _____ < 44 | 94 < _____ |

8. Tell or write the time in two ways: (1) using the expressions *o'clock* or *half past* and (2) with numbers.

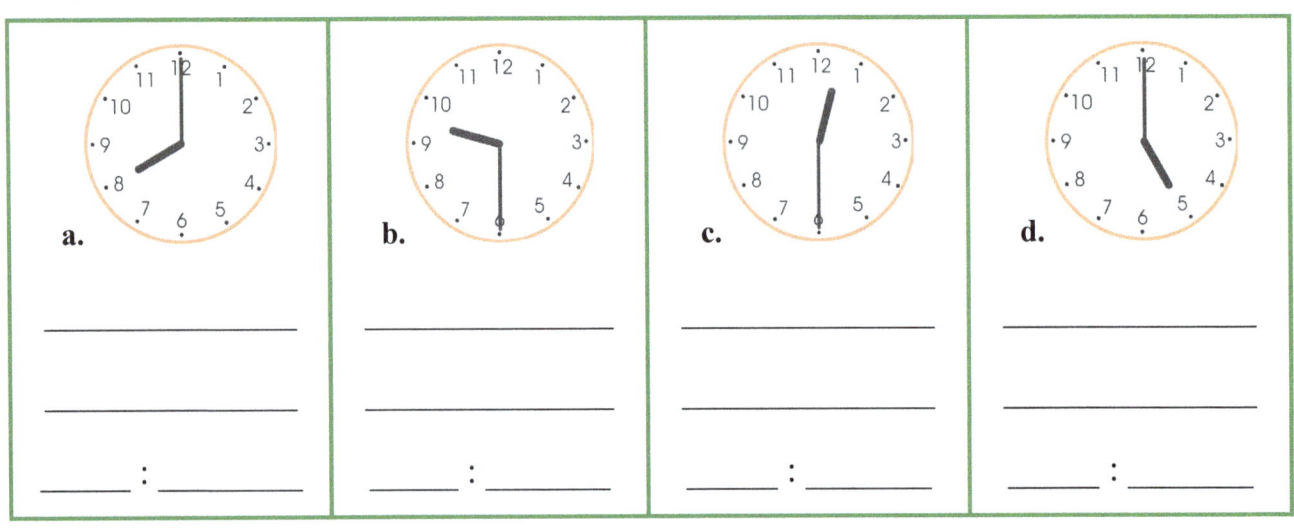

a. _____ _____ ____ : ____

b. _____ _____ ____ : ____

c. _____ _____ ____ : ____

d. _____ _____ ____ : ____

# Chapter 5 Review

1. **a.** Connect each pair of numbers that add up to 7. Which number is left by itself?

```
    1  7    4
  3     2      5
     6   5      2
  0   3      6    4
```

**b.** Connect each pair of numbers that add up to 8. Which number is left by itself?

```
   5  6    2    7
        0   2
      3   5      6
   1   8    4
```

2. Fill in the missing numbers. Draw lines to connect the facts that belong to the same fact family.

| | | |
|---|---|---|
| 9 – _____ = 7 | 9 = _____ + 2 | 9 – _____ = 5 |
| 9 – _____ = 6 | 9 = 8 + _____ | 9 – 6 = _____ |
| 9 – 1 = _____ | 9 = _____ + 5 | 9 – _____ = 2 |
| 9 – _____ = 4 | 9 = 3 + _____ | _____ + 8 = 9 |

3. Subtract.

| a. | b. | c. |
|---|---|---|
| 5 – 2 – 3 = _____ | 8 – 4 – 1 = _____ | 7 – 2 – 4 = _____ |
| 10 – 1 – 6 = _____ | 8 – 2 – 2 = _____ | 10 – 1 – 6 = _____ |

4. Write what the missing number equals.

| | | |
|---|---|---|
| **a.** 6 – ⬤ = 1 | **b.** 3 + ⬤ = 9 | **c.** 7 – ⬤ = 2 |
| ⬤ = _____ | ⬤ = _____ | ⬤ = _____ |

5. Fill in the missing numbers. Draw lines to connect the facts that belong to the same fact family.

| | | |
|---|---|---|
| $10 - \underline{\quad} = 8$ | $\underline{\quad} + 9 = 10$ | $\underline{\quad} + 1 = 10$ |
| $10 - \underline{\quad} = 5$ | $4 + \underline{\quad} = 10$ | $10 - 5 = \underline{\quad}$ |
| $10 - \underline{\quad} = 1$ | $5 + \underline{\quad} = 10$ | $10 - 4 = \underline{\quad}$ |
| $10 - 3 = \underline{\quad}$ | $2 + \underline{\quad} = 10$ | $\underline{\quad} + 3 = 10$ |
| $10 - 6 = \underline{\quad}$ | $\underline{\quad} + 7 = 10$ | $10 - \underline{\quad} = 2$ |

6. Time to play teacher again! Three children worked some problems.
   Check their work and correct any that are wrong.

| Kayla: | Diego: | Malik: |
|---|---|---|
| a. $5 - 0 = 5$ | c. $9 - 4 = 4$ | e. $3 = 7 - 4$ |
| b. $10 - 3 = 6$ | d. $2 = 6 - 8$ | f. $7 - 6 = 2$ |

7. Compare, writing <, > or = in the box.

   a. $7 + 3$ ☐ $2 + 8$     b. $5 - 1$ ☐ $1 + 4$     c. $8$ ☐ $10 - 3$

8. Solve. Write an addition or a subtraction equation for each problem.

| |
|---|
| a. There were four birds in a tree. Four more flew in. How many birds are there now? $\underline{\quad} \boxed{\phantom{x}} \underline{\quad} = \underline{\quad}$<br><br>There are \underline{\quad} birds now. |
| b. Look! Five of them just flew away! How many birds are there now? $\underline{\quad} \boxed{\phantom{x}} \underline{\quad} = \underline{\quad}$<br><br>There are \underline{\quad} birds now. |

# Chapter 6: Shapes and Fractions
## Introduction

This sixth chapter of *Math Mammoth Grade 1* covers basic shapes, composing and decomposing shapes, and halves and fourths.

Children explore basic properties of shapes, such as the number of sides, whether the shape has right angles ("square" corners), or whether some of its sides are the same length. Then they also compose and decompose geometric figures. This means, for example, putting two triangles together to make a quadrilateral, or dividing a square into two triangles. Composing and decomposing figures helps children understand part-whole relationships as well as observe and learn the properties of the original and composite shapes.

The lessons in this chapter can seem quite easy, but they are laying a proper foundation for geometric understanding in later years. For example, composing and decomposing shapes helps develop a foundation for understanding area (studied in 3rd grade and onward). Analyzing the properties of shapes, such as the presence or absence of right angles or sides that are the same length, prepares students to study congruence. Dividing shapes into parts helps to build an understanding of part-whole relationships for the study of fractions. And this is why we study fractions in this chapter — fractions arise from dividing a whole (such as a shape) into equal parts.

Don't forget to also check out the videos at https://www.mathmammoth.com/videos/ .

### Good Mathematical Practices

* Mathematics has a lot to do with structures and patterns. In this chapter, students begin classifying (sorting) shapes based on their properties. This task of analyzing and sorting shapes continues all through the elementary school, and it is typical of the work that mathematicians do: look for patterns or structures.


## Pacing Suggestion for Chapter 6

Please add one day to the pacing for the test if you will use it.

| The Lessons in Chapter 6 | page | span | suggested pacing | your pacing |
|---|---|---|---|---|
| Basic Shapes 1 ............................................... | 50 | *2 pages* | 1 day | |
| Basic Shapes 2 ............................................... | 52 | *3 pages* | 1 day | |
| Basic Shapes 3 ............................................... | 55 | *3 pages* | 1 day | |
| Solids ............................................................. | 59 | *2 pages* | 1 day | |
| Composing Shapes ........................................ | 63 | *2 pages* | 1 day | |
| Composing and Decomposing Shapes 1 ......... | 64 | *2 pages* | 1 day | |
| Composing and Decomposing Shapes 2 ......... | 66 | *2 pages* | 1 day | |
| Halves and Quarters, Part 1 ........................... | 68 | *2 pages* | 1 day | |
| Halves and Quarters, Part 2 ........................... | 70 | *3 pages* | 1-2 days | |
| Chapter 6 Mixed Review ............................... | 73 | *2 pages* | 1 day | |
| Chapter 6 Review .......................................... | 75 | *2 pages* | 1 day | |
| Chapter 6 Test (optional) | | | | |
| **TOTALS** | | *25 pages* | 11-12 days | |

# Math Talks

Shapes and fractions are great topics for "math talks." Remember to also look for shapes and fractions around you, and ask your child or students to do so.

https://www.mathmammoth.com/MathTalks

# Games and Activities

### Free Drawing

**You need:** paper, pencil, ruler

Ask the child to draw a certain number of dots on the paper, such as four or five, and then connect those with line segments (using a ruler!) to get a shape. Then the child can divide this shape into smaller shapes by drawing more lines. What shapes do they get? Encourage the child to experiment freely with such drawings.

### Pattern Blocks/Tangram

A set of pattern blocks or a tangram game, where children use shapes to make new composite shapes, is something all children love. The list of further Internet resources gives links to free online versions. The below links give examples of sets on Amazon, but there are many more available. Look for a set that comes with pattern cards.

**Coogam Wooden Pattern Blocks Set 130PCS**
https://www.amazon.com/dp/B07MYYK64R/?tag=mathmammoth-20

**LOVESTOWN 230 Pcs Wooden Pattern Blocks**
https://www.amazon.com/dp/B08C37JMP2/?tag=mathmammoth-20

## Games and Activities at Math Mammoth Practice Zone

**Sort the Shapes**
Drag each shape to the correct box.
https://www.mathmammoth.com/practice/sorting-game#questions=6&sort-by=shape

**Fraction Matcher**
Match a visual model of a fractions with another visual model of the same fraction, or with the fraction written with numbers. Choose Level 1.
https://www.mathmammoth.com/practice/fraction-matcher

48

## Further Resources on the Internet

We have compiled a list of Internet resources that match the topics in this chapter, including pages that offer:

- **online practice** for concepts;
- online **games**, or occasionally, printable games;
- **animations** and interactive **illustrations** of math concepts;
- **articles** that teach a math concept.

We heartily recommend you take a look! Many of our customers love using these resources to supplement the bookwork. You can use these resources as you see fit for extra practice, to illustrate a concept better and even just for some fun. Enjoy!

https://l.mathmammoth.com/2026/gr1ch6

# Basic Shapes 1

These are **triangles**.
A triangle has three sides
(and three corners).

These are **circles**. A circle
doesn't have any corners.

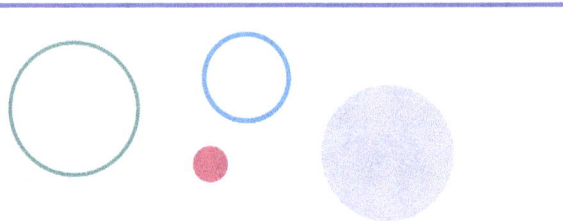

1. Is this a triangle? What do you think?

2. Is this a triangle? Why or why not?

3. Is this a circle? Why or why not?

What makes a shape to be a **triangle**?

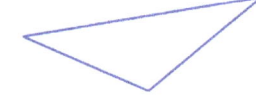

- A triangle has three sides.
- The sides are straight,
  not round or curved.
- A triangle is a closed shape.

What makes a shape to be a **circle**?

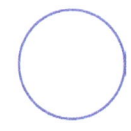

- A circle is perfectly round, with
  the same roundness everywhere!
- A circle is a closed shape.

(Mathematically, a circle is the set of points
that are at the same distance from the center
point of the circle, and this distance is called
the radius of the circle.)

4. Color all the triangles and circles.

5. Sketch (draw) here two different triangles. One way to draw a triangle is to first draw three dots, and then join them with lines.

| Triangle 1: | Triangle 2: |
|---|---|
|  |  |

6. Draw here (freehand, sketching) a shape that is *not* a circle, yet it is round.

7. Draw here (freehand, sketching) three shapes that are *not* triangles.

# Basic Shapes 2

These are rectangles. A **rectangle** has four straight sides, and is a closed shape.

A rectangle also has four "square" corners. This means that each corner of a rectangle is like a corner of a postcard (or of a book). (The mathematical term is a "right angle".)

Here, we can exactly fit a corner of a postcard into a corner of this rectangle, so the corner is a "square" corner (a right angle).

The corner of a postcard does not exactly fit into the corner of either shape. The shapes are not rectangles.

We can mark the corners of a rectangle with little squares, to show that the corners are right angles.

1. Do these shapes have square corners (right angles)? Check with a postcard or a thin book. Mark the corners of the rectangles with little squares.

a.

b.

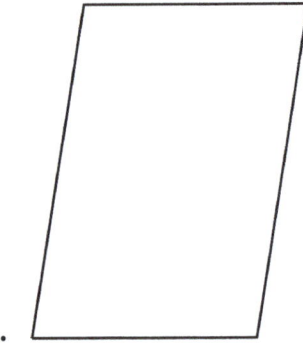

c.

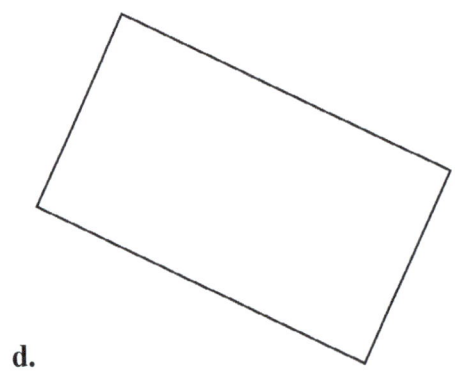

d.

 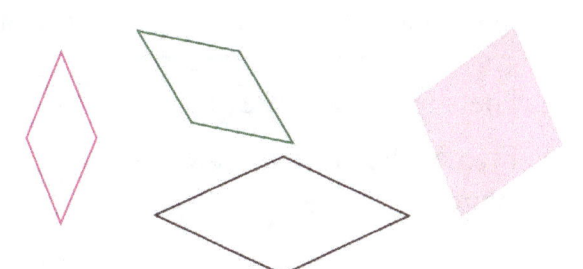

These are **squares**. Like rectangles, squares also have four sides and four "square" corners (right angles). In addition to that, their four sides are <u>the same length</u>.

These are **diamond shapes**. The mathematical term is a rhombus (pl. rhombi). They have four sides that are the same length.

2. Find all the squares and diamond shapes, and color them with colors you like. Mark the right angles of the squares with little squares.

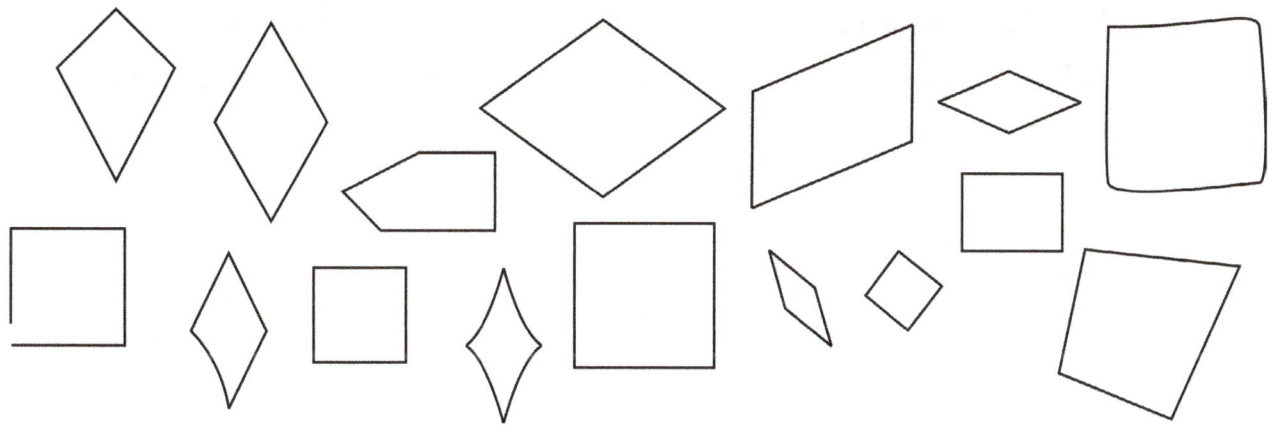

3. Find all the rectangles and color them. Mark their corners with little squares.

53

4. Draw a closed shape with straight sides that fits the given rules.
   (Sketching or approximate drawing is sufficient.)

| | |
|---|---|
| **a.** • The shape has three sides.<br>    • Two of the sides are the same length. | **b.** • The shape has three sides.<br>    • Each side is the same length |
| **c.** • The shape has four sides.<br>    • Each side is the same length | **d.** • The shape has four sides.<br>    • Each corner is a "square" corner. |
| **e.** • The shape has four sides.<br>    • Each corner is a "square" corner.<br>    • Each side is the same length. | **f.** • The shape has five sides. |

# Basic Shapes 3

If a four-sided (closed) shape is not a rectangle, a square, or a diamond, you can simply call it a "**four-sided shape.**"

The mathematical term is a **quadrilateral.**
"Quadri-" comes from *quattuor,* Latin for "four."
"Lateral" comes from *lateralis*, Latin for "side."

A six-sided closed shape is called a **hexagon**. The word "hex" in the Greek language means six. A "hexagon" is simply Greek for six-cornered shape. See some hexagons on the right.

There are Greek names for shapes with 5, 7, 8, 9, or 10 sides also. (Ask your teacher for those.) For example, the shape with 8 sides is an octagon.("Octa" means 8 in Greek; think *octopus* with its eight legs).

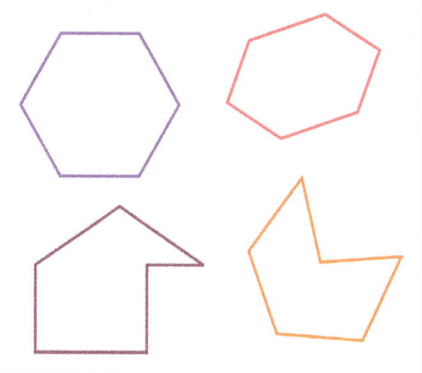

1. Sort the shapes on the last page of this lesson by the number of sides.
   You can cut out the shapes and sort them manually, or, not cut them out and use color or other markings. For example, you could color the triangles red, the four-sided shapes green, the five-sided shapes blue, and the hexagons purple.

2. **Activity.** You need: a bunch of pencils, pens, and crayons. At least six of them should be of the same length, and others should be of various lengths. Use them to build shapes that fit the conditions below. (Optionally, you can sketch your creations below.)

| **a.** • The shape has five sides. | **b.** • The shape has four sides. |
|---|---|
| **c.** • The shape has four sides.<br>• Two of the sides are the same length | **d.** • The shape has six sides.<br>• Each side is the same length. |

3. Again, use the pencils and pens to build shapes that fit the conditions below.

| | |
|---|---|
| **a.** • The shape has six sides. | **b.** • The shape has four sides.<br>• Each side is the same length. |
| **c.** • The shape has three sides.<br>• Each side is the same length. | **d.** • The shape has four sides.<br>• Each corner is a "square" corner. |

4. Copy the shape in the grid on the right.

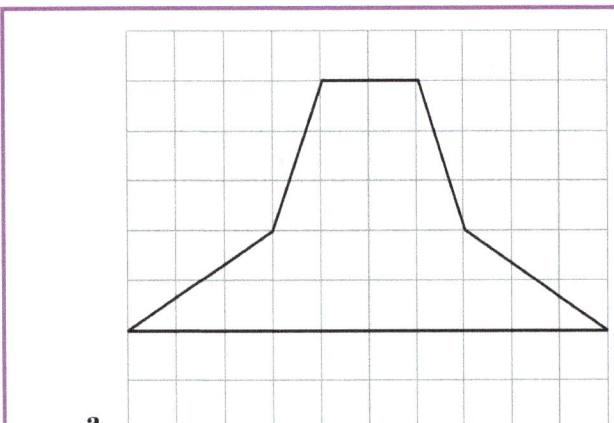

**a.**

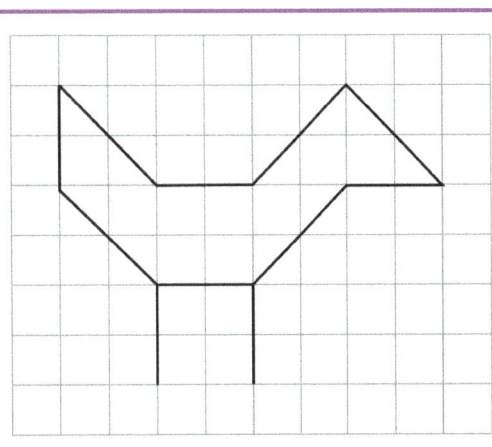

**b.**

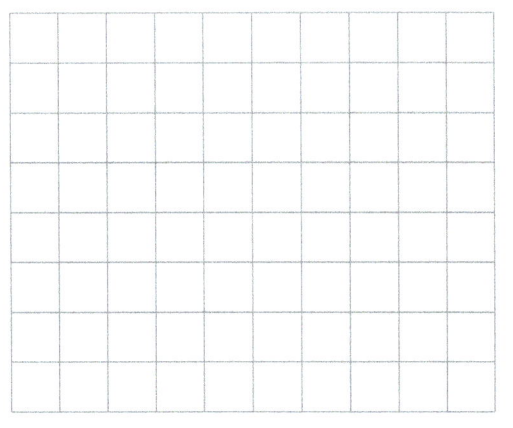

56

# Shapes to sort for exercise #1

https://www.mathmammoth.com/download/sort-shapes-gr1.pdf

(This page is left blank intentionally.)

# Solids

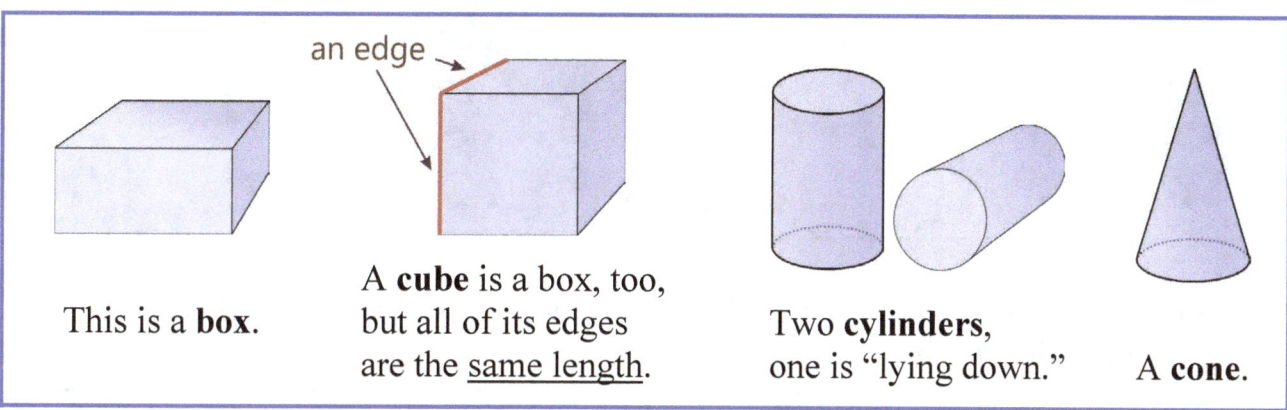

an edge →

This is a **box**.

A **cube** is a box, too, but all of its edges are the <u>same length</u>.

Two **cylinders**, one is "lying down."

A **cone**.

1. Name the basic solid(s) in these objects.

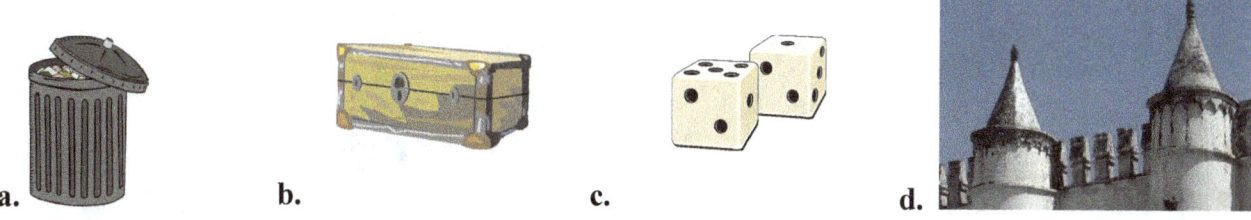

a.　　　　b.　　　　c.　　　　d.

2. Which solid is it?

   **a.** It has six edges. It has six faces (flat sides) that are squares.

   **b.** It has a circle at the bottom and at the top.

   **c.** It has a circle at the bottom and a pointed top.

   **d.** It has six edges. All of its faces (flat sides) are rectangles or squares.

3. **Activity.** You will need a set of geometric solids, or solids you have made by folding from paper. Build these shapes (or similar) using the solids in your set.

a.　　　　b.　　　　c.

4. **Activity.** First, build the given shape. Then build a *larger* shape (of your own choice) that has that shape as a part of it.

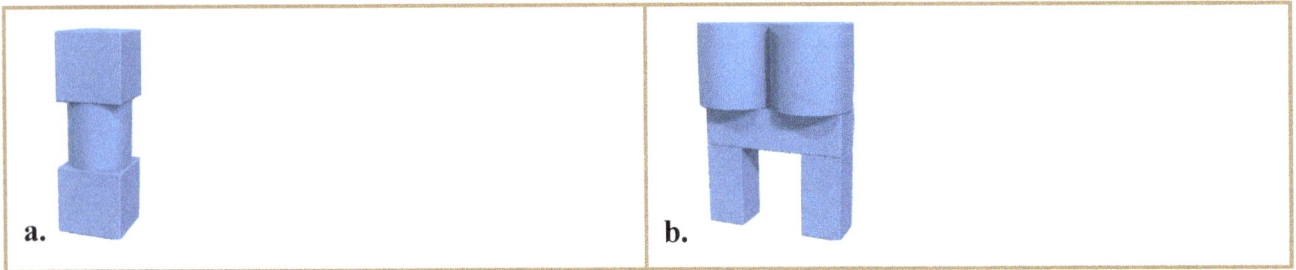

a.

b.

5. If you have the shapes on the left, which of the two shapes from the right can you build? Look at the table one row at a time.

| If you have these: | Which shape can you build? |
|---|---|
| a. | or ? |
| b. | or ? |
| c. | or ? |
| d. | or ? |

60

*This page intentionally left blank.*

# Composing Shapes

**Activity.** Cut out the shapes on the previous page. You can also download them from
https://www.mathmammoth.com/download/cutout-shapes-gr1.pdf

<u>Hint</u>: if you have the download version of the curriculum, you can print the page of shapes in landscape orientation, scaled at 140-150% (depending on the margins your printer sets), so it prints on two sheets of paper. All the shapes will then be much bigger.

1. Make a big triangle with four yellow triangles (marked with 1).

2. Take all six of the yellow triangles (marked with 1).
   Put them together to get a hexagon.

3. Use two shapes to make a square.

4. Use *three* shapes to make a square.

5. Make a bigger square than the one you made in #4, using any pieces you choose.

6. Make a rectangle using two shapes.

7. Make a rectangle using four shapes.

8. Put together two of the green triangles (#4) to get a four-sided shape. Do this in several different ways!

9. Use the two slim rectangles (#3) to make **a.** a rectangle; **b.** an L-shape; **c.** an eight-sided shape.

10. Put together the two purple shapes (#6) to make a six-sided shape (a hexagon). You can do this in several different ways!

11. Put together the two purple shapes (#6) to make a quadrilateral.

12. A challenge: put together the two purple shapes (#6) to make a *pentagon* (a five-sided shape).

13. Make your own pentagons using any of the shapes! Make several different ones.

14. Make your own hexagons using any of the shapes! Make several different ones.

15. Make interesting figures of your own using any of the shapes. Have fun!

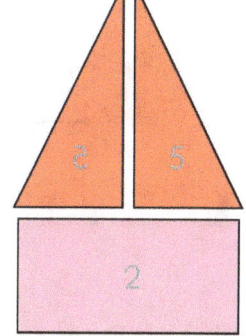

# Composing and Decomposing Shapes 1

1. Draw a line from dot to dot so that you divide the shape into <u>two new shapes</u>.
   What kind of shapes are the new shapes?

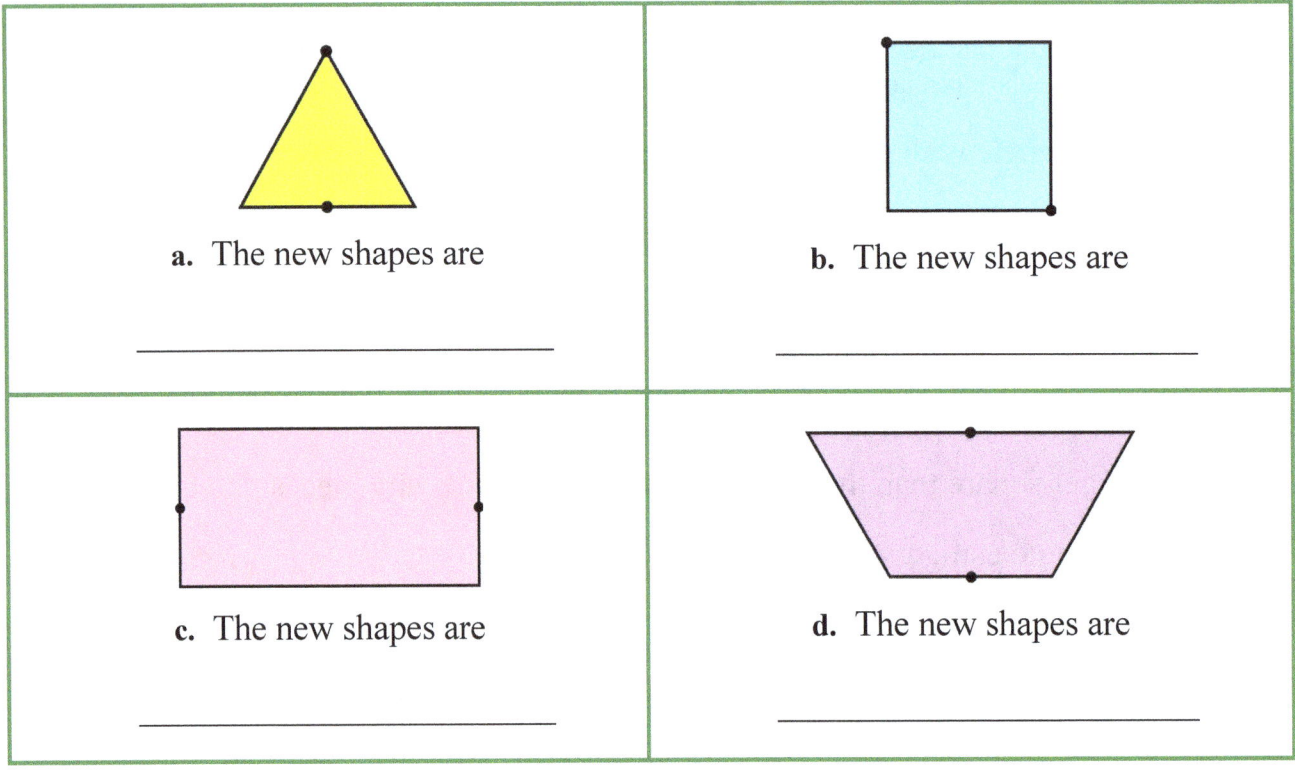

a. The new shapes are

_____

b. The new shapes are

_____

c. The new shapes are

_____

d. The new shapes are

_____

2. Draw *one* or *two* lines in each shape so that you get new shapes as indicated.
   Instead of doing this with a pencil, you can draw the basic shapes on paper (they don't need
   to be the same size as here), cut them out, and use scissors to cut each shape into parts.

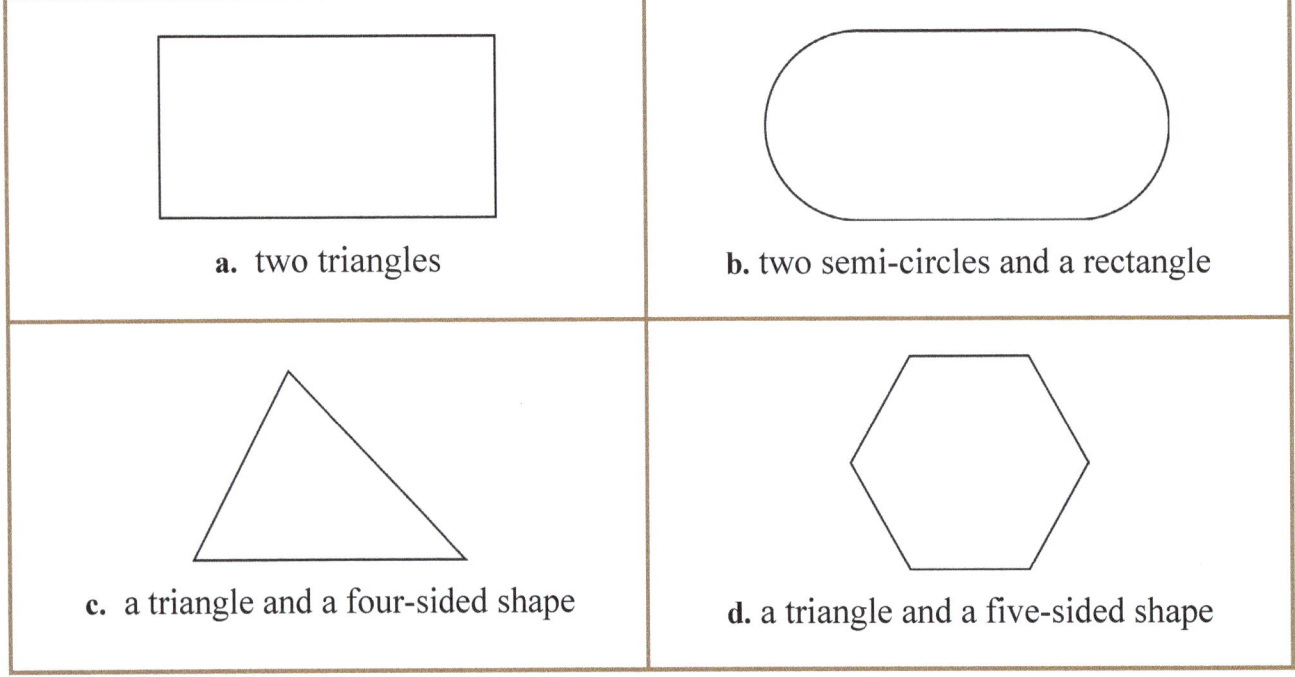

a. two triangles

b. two semi-circles and a rectangle

c. a triangle and a four-sided shape

d. a triangle and a five-sided shape

3. How many squares can you find in this figure?

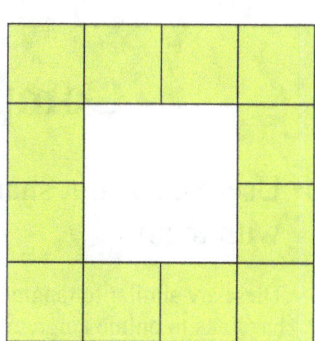

4. How many rectangles can you find in this figure?

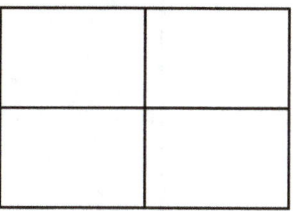

5. Divide each shape into simple shapes by drawing lines in it. Name each shape you get!

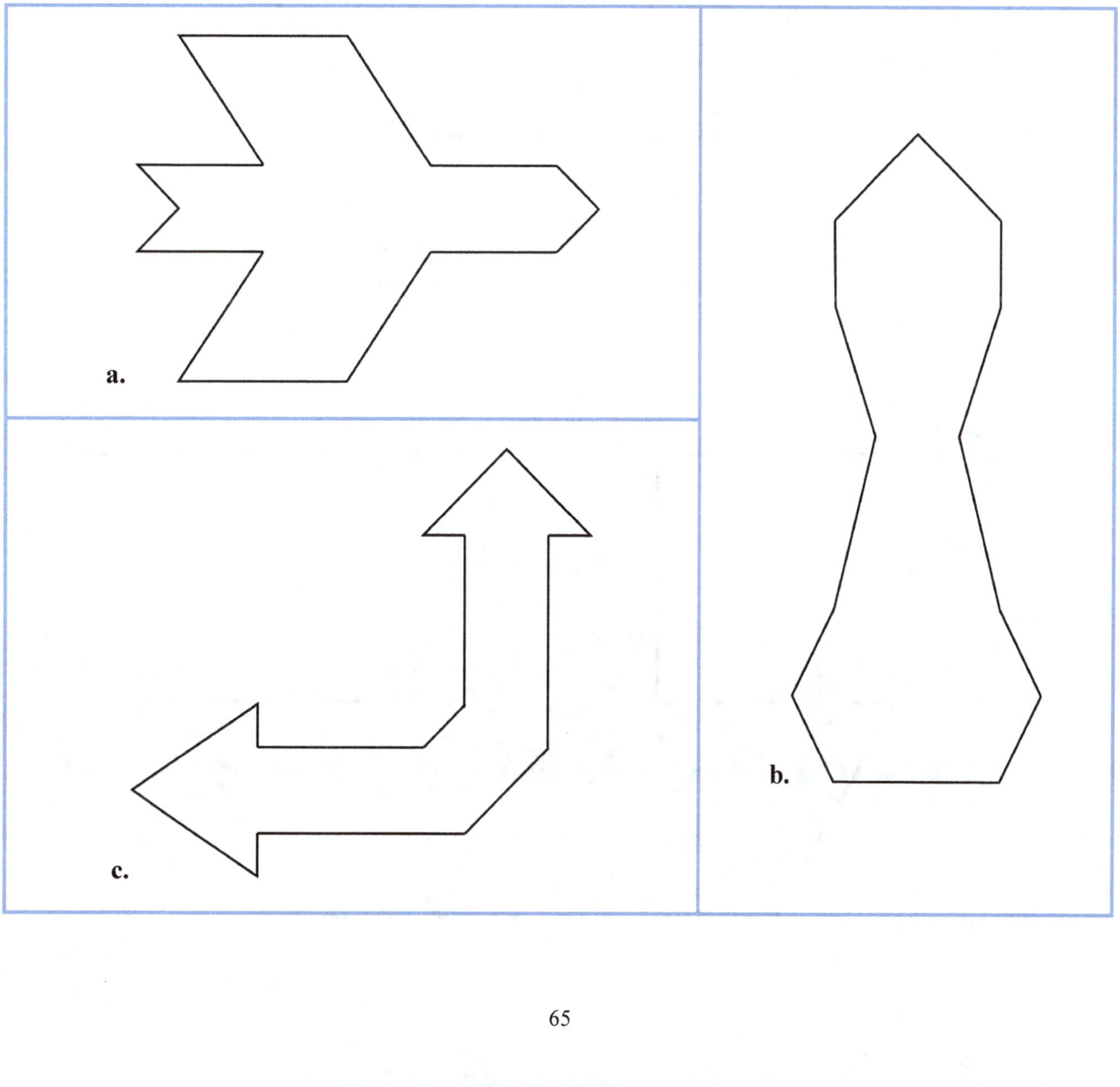

a.

b.

c.

65

# Composing and Decomposing Shapes 2

1. Use the cut-out shapes from the lesson "Composing Shapes". Make these shapes with them.

These are similar to tangram puzzles. Our list of Internet resources (https://l.mathmammoth.com/2026/gr1ch6) has links to online tangram games. Physical tangram sets are lots of fun — see the chapter introduction for some ideas.

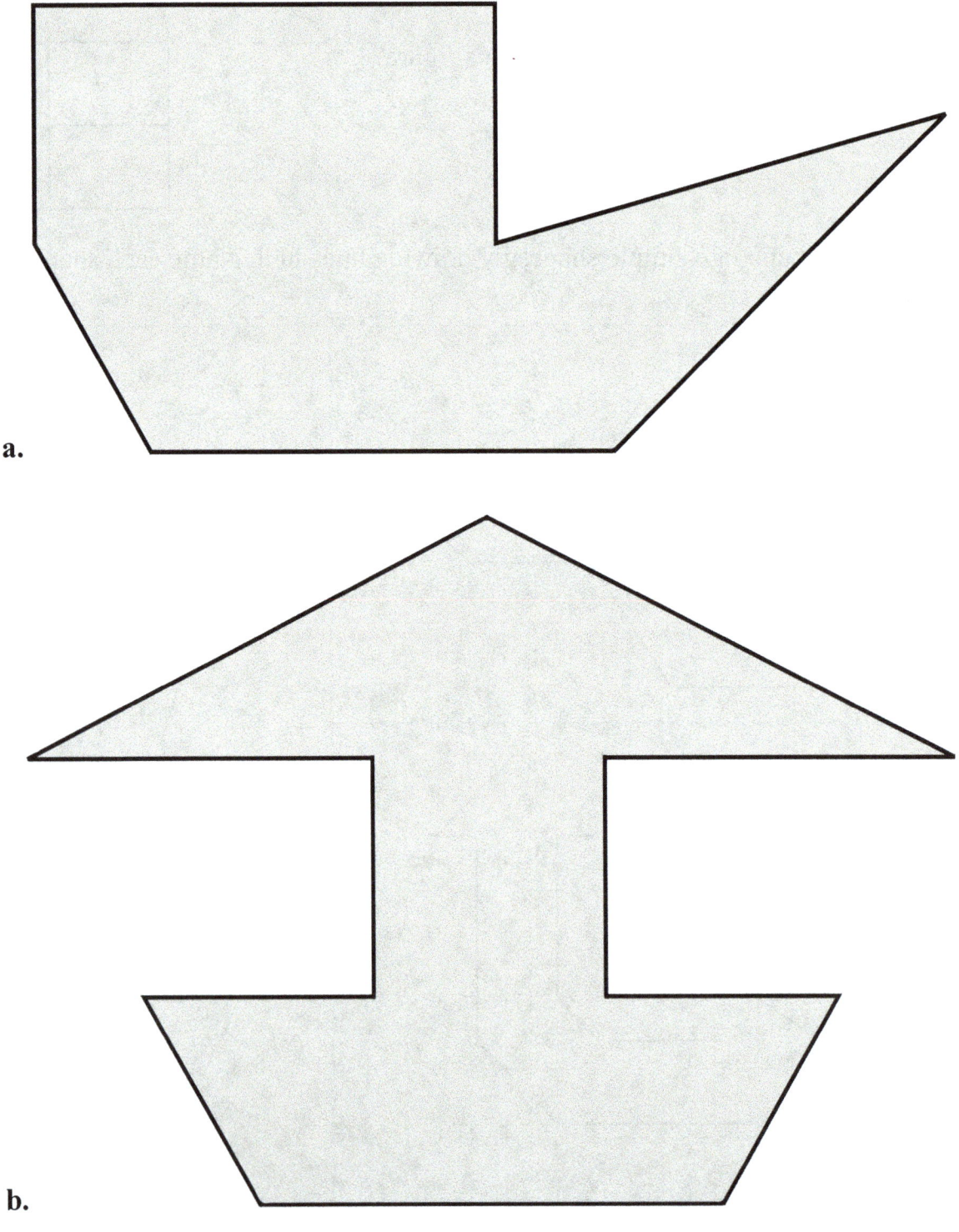

a.

b.

2. The figures below are all quadrilaterals (four-sided shapes). In each shape, draw a line from one corner to the opposite corner. Then draw another line from corner to corner in each shape, using the two other corners you didn't yet use.

   How many parts does each four-sided shape have now? _____

   What kind of shapes are these parts? _____

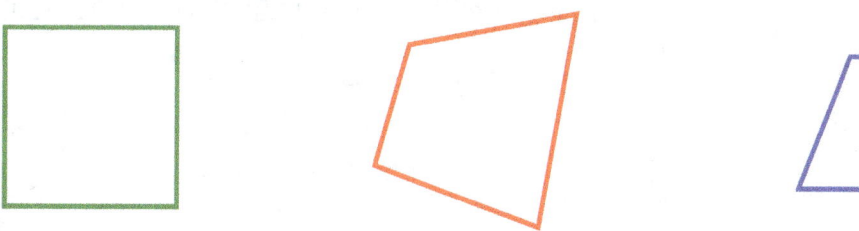

3. **Activity — shape puzzles!** Take a regular sheet of paper (letter size or A4). Fold it in half horizontally. Then fold it in half again so you get a rectangle. Then open it and cut along the crease lines to get four identical rectangles. Optionally you may shade each rectangle with a color.

   Now cut each rectangle into 3-6 pieces to make a puzzle, and give the pieces to someone else to assemble back as a rectangle.

4. Here are two more tangram puzzles you can do with the cutout shapes. These figures are not to scale but are only half the size of the real shapes.

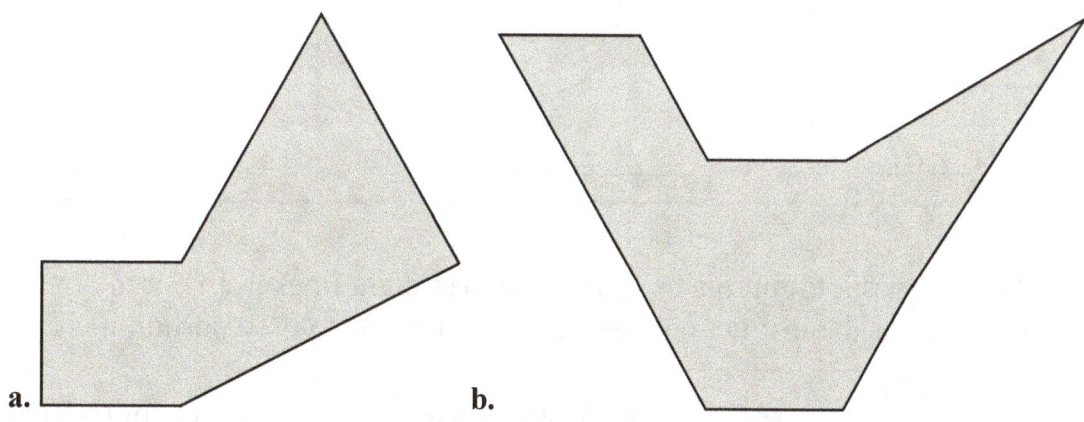

a.                                    b.

---

**Puzzle Corner**  How many triangles can you find in this figure? Look carefully!

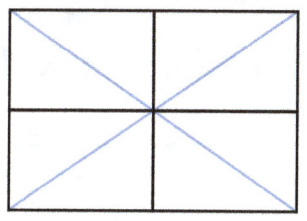

67

# Halves and Quarters, Part 1

Each square below is divided into *two* equal parts or two equal shares. The parts are called **halves**. Each part is <u>one half</u>.

Here, **one-half** of the square is colored. The other half is white.

Here, **both halves** are colored. The two halves make up the whole square.

Each circle below is divided into *four* equal parts or four equal shares. The parts are called ***fourths*** or ***quarters***. Each part is <u>one quarter</u> or <u>one fourth</u>.

Here, three-fourths of the circle is colored. One quarter is white.

Here, all four quarters are colored. The four quarters make up the whole circle.

1. Divide these shapes into halves by drawing a straight line from dot to dot. Then color them as the instructions say. Lastly name the colored portion.

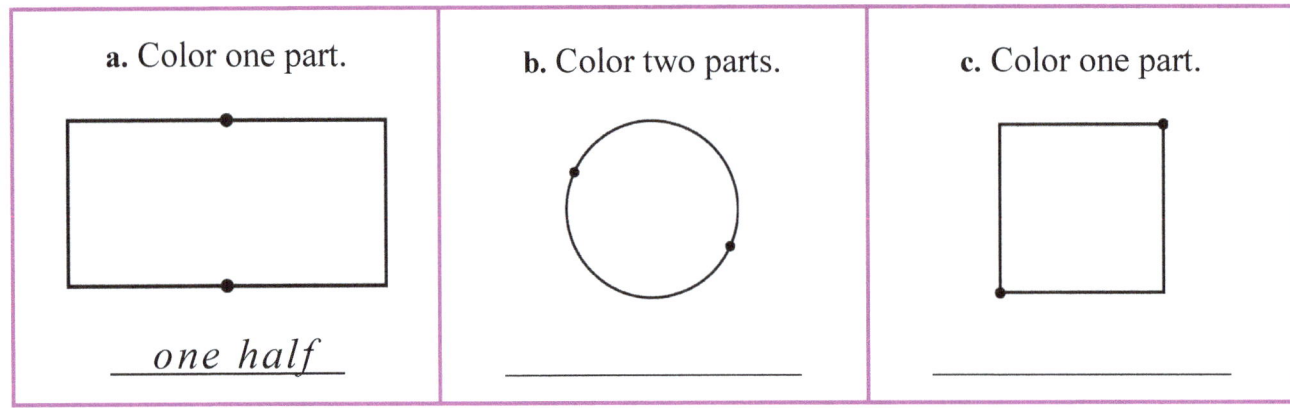

**a.** Color one part.

**b.** Color two parts.

**c.** Color one part.

*one half*

_____

_____

2. Divide these shapes into fourths by drawing two straight lines from dot to dot. Then color them as the instructions say. Lastly name the colored portion.

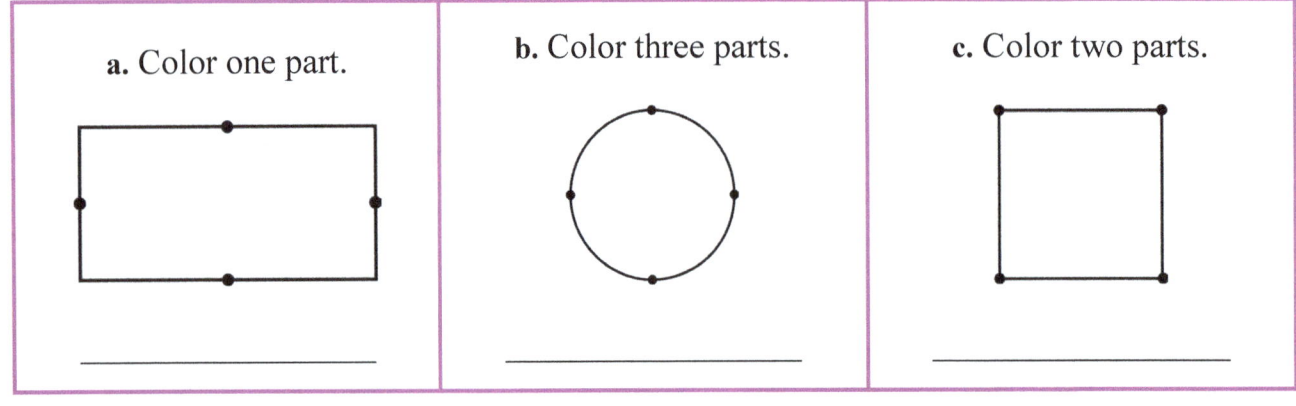

**a.** Color one part.

**b.** Color three parts.

**c.** Color two parts.

_____

_____

_____

3. Name the colored portion.

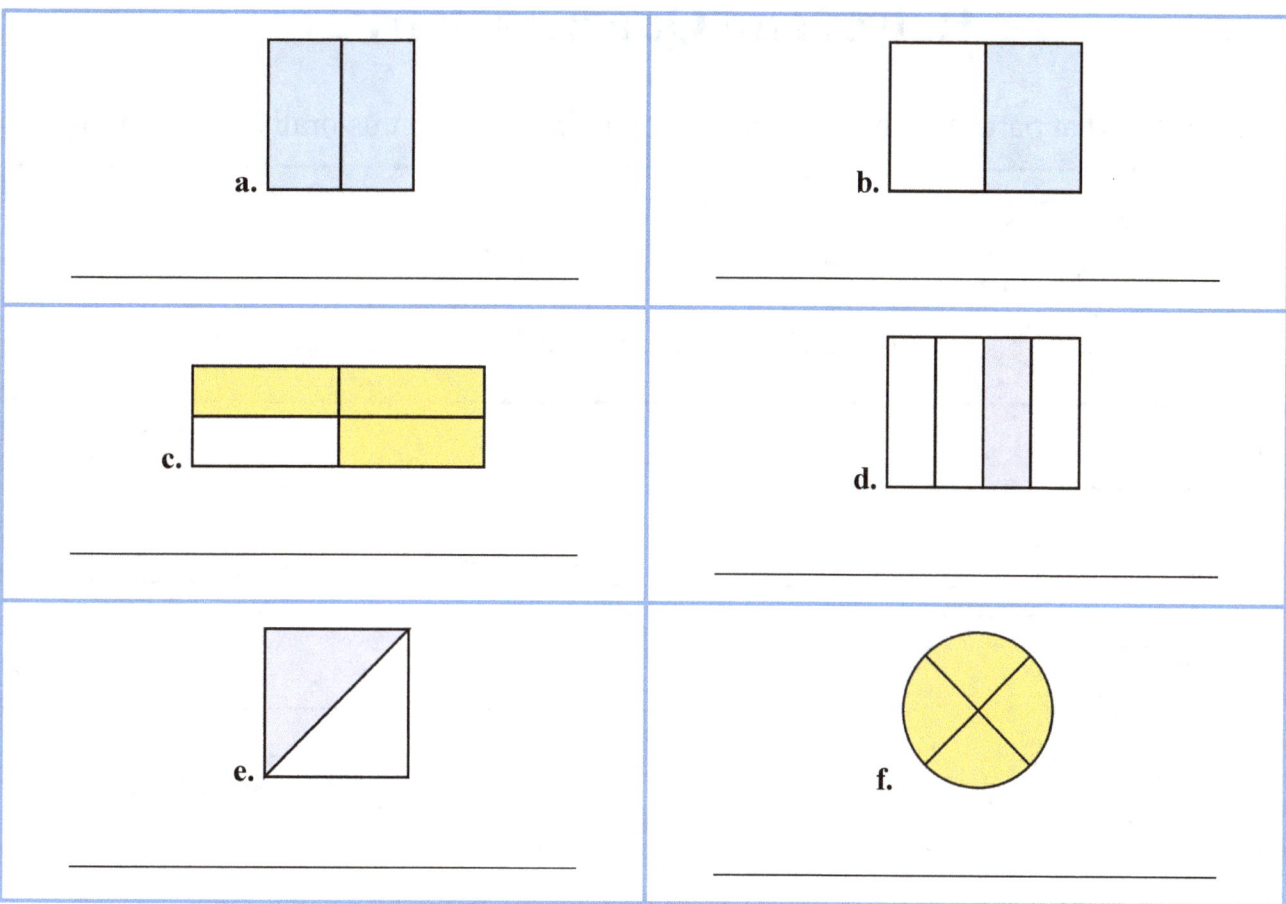

a. _____

b. _____

c. _____

d. _____

e. _____

f. _____

4. First divide the shape into equal shares, then color.

| a. Color 1 fourth. | b. Color 3 fourths. | c. Color 2 halves. | d. Color 4 fourths. |
|---|---|---|---|
| e. Color 1 half. | f. Color 1 fourth. | g. Color 2 fourths. | h. Color 2 halves. |

# Halves and Quarters, Part 2

1. Describe what part(s) of the shape are colored. You can do this orally or in writing.

**a.**
_____1_____ _____fourth_____ of

the _____circle_____ is colored.

**b.**
_____ _____ of

the _____ are colored.

**c.**
_____ _____ of

the _____ are colored.

**d.**
_____ _____ of

the _____ is colored.

**e.**
_____ _____ of

the _____ are colored.

**f.**
_____ _____ of

the _____ are colored.

2. Suzanne divided this circle into two parts and said, "This is one-half of the circle." Do you agree with her? Explain.

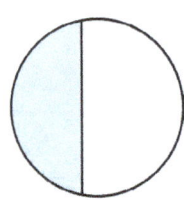

3. Describe what portion of what thing you see (e.g. one-half of a pear).

4. First divide the shape into equal shares, then color.

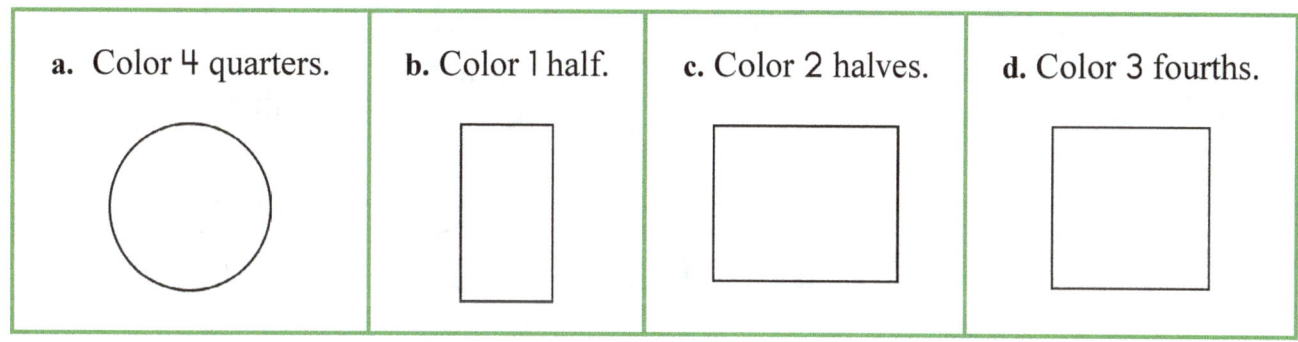

**a.** Color 4 quarters.  **b.** Color 1 half.  **c.** Color 2 halves.  **d.** Color 3 fourths.

5. Which is more? Color pieces to help you.

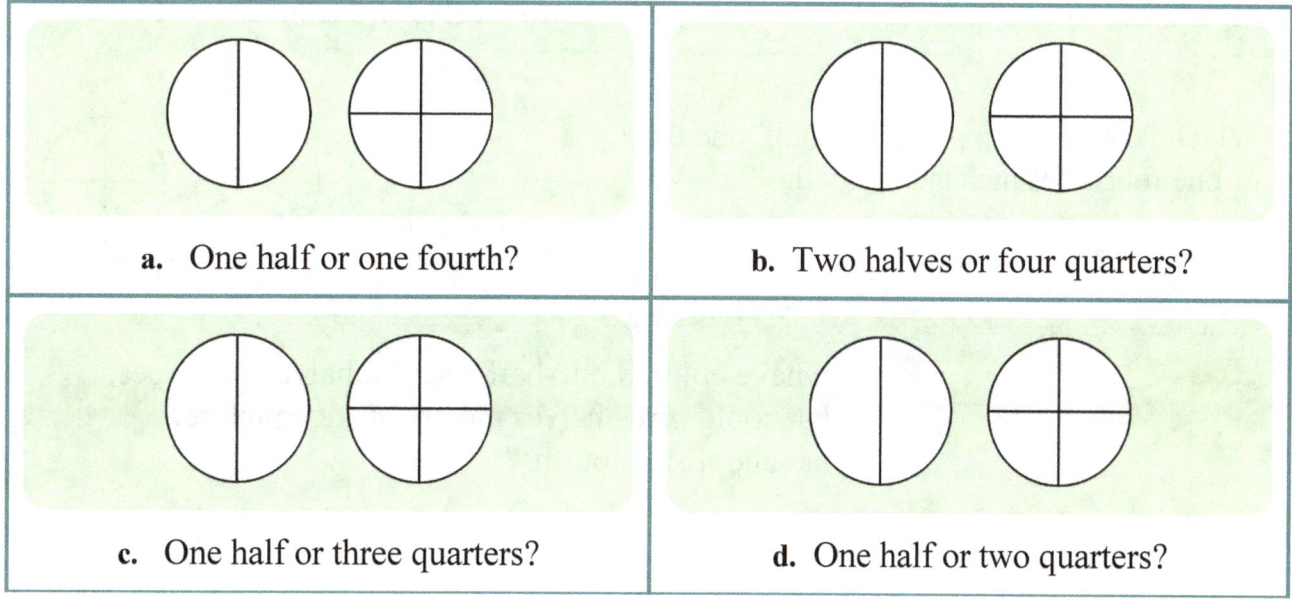

**a.** One half or one fourth?    **b.** Two halves or four quarters?

**c.** One half or three quarters?    **d.** One half or two quarters?

*(The instruction and exercises about thirds are optional.)*

This square is divided into three parts that are the same.
The parts are **thirds**. Each part is <u>one third</u>.

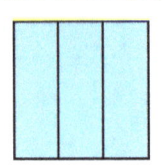

6. Color.

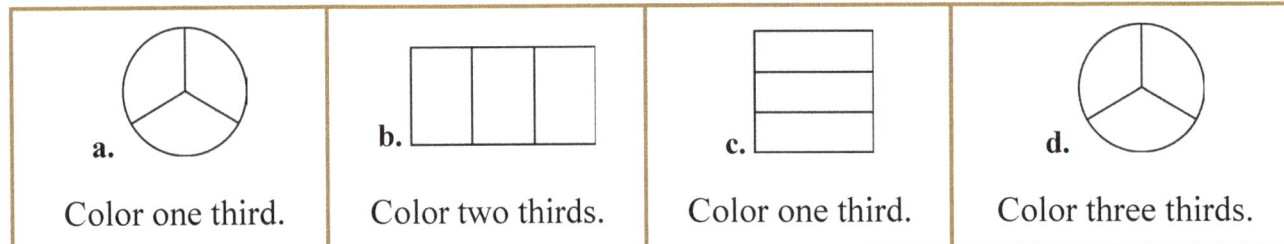

**a.** Color one third.

**b.** Color two thirds.

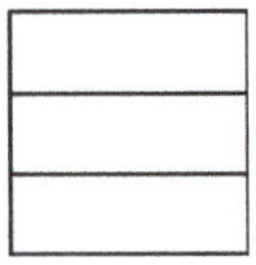

**c.** Color one third.

**d.** Color three thirds.

7. Compare. Color pieces to help you.

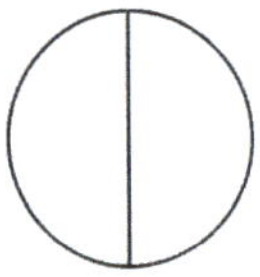

**a.** Which is more:
two thirds or one half?

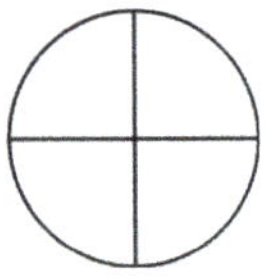

**b.** Which is more:
three fourths or two thirds?

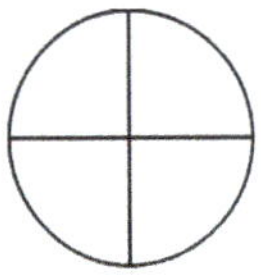

**c.** Which is more:
two thirds or two quarters?

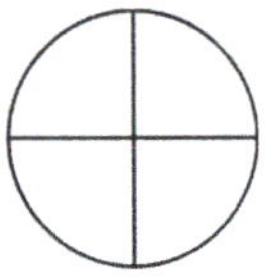

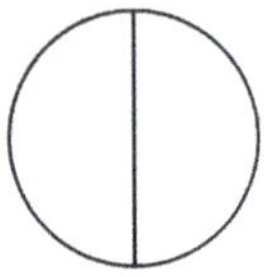

**d.** Which is more:
two fourths or one half?

8. Which is the biggest piece, one half, one third,
or one fourth? Which is the smallest?

**Puzzle Corner**   You have colored one-half and two halves of shapes.
What could *three* halves mean? Make a picture.
What about five fourths?

# Chapter 6 Mixed Review

1. Find the difference between the numbers. Then write an addition.

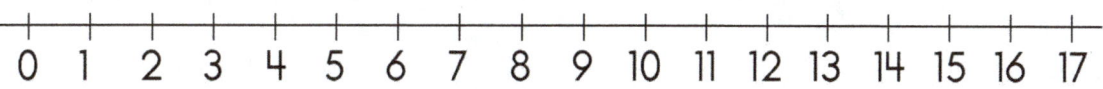

| **a.** from 6 to 10 | **b.** from 4 to 7 | **c.** from 6 to 11 |
|---|---|---|
| _____ steps | _____ steps | _____ steps |
| 6 + _____ = 10 | 4 + _____ = 7 | 6 + _____ = 11 |

2. Tell the time, using numbers. Include AM or PM.

| | | |
|---|---|---|
|  | |  |
| **a.** People are sleeping. | **b.** Lily is eating lunch. | **c.** Dad goes to the post office. |
| _____ : _____ _____ | _____ : _____ _____ | _____ : _____ _____ |

3. Subtract. Compare the two problems and their results.

| **a.** | **b.** | **c.** |
|---|---|---|
| 9 – 3 – 3 = _____ | 7 – 2 – 2 = _____ | 10 – 6 – 1 = _____ |
| 8 – 3 – 3 = _____ | 7 – 2 – 1 = _____ | 9 – 6 – 1 = _____ |

4. Which numbers add up to 8? Find the additions that are wrong.

| 8 = 5 + 3 | 8 = 0 + 8 | 8 = 1 + 7 |
|---|---|---|
| 8 = 2 + 7 | 8 = 6 + 1 | 8 = 3 + 6 |

5. Which equation matches the word problem? Solve.

| | |
|---|---|
| **a.** Amelia drew four stars on paper.<br>Bill drew two more stars than Amelia.<br>How many did Bill draw? | $2 +$ _____ $= 4$<br><br>$4 + 2 =$ _____<br><br>$4 - 2 =$ _____ |
| **b.** Mom baked 10 muffins.<br>But now there are only six left.<br>How many were eaten? | $6 + 10 =$ _____<br><br>_____ $- 10 = 6$<br><br>$10 -$ _____ $= 6$ |

6. Circle each group of ten dots. Then count the groups of ten and the ones left over.
   Write the number with a numeral. Also, tell *or* write the name of the number.

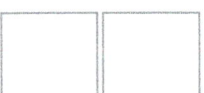

tens    ones

**a.** _____

_____

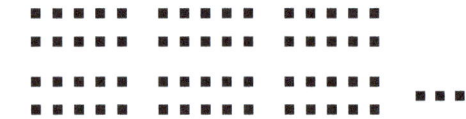
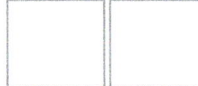

tens    ones

**b.** _____

_____

7. Count by ones from 111, filling in the missing numbers.

| 111 | | | | 115 | | | | | |
|---|---|---|---|---|---|---|---|---|---|

8. Solve.

| | | |
|---|---|---|
| **a.** $40 + 30 =$ _____ | **b.** $50 + 30 =$ _____ | **c.** $80 - 20 =$ _____ |
| $50 + 50 =$ _____ | $60 - 50 =$ _____ | $100 - 40 =$ _____ |

# Chapter 6 Review

1. Divide the shape...

| **a.** ...into a triangle and a five-sided shape. | **b.** ...into a square and a rectangle. | **c.** ... into a four-sided shape and a triangle. |
|---|---|---|
| 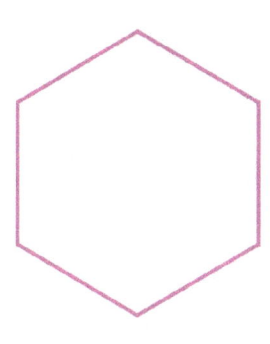 | 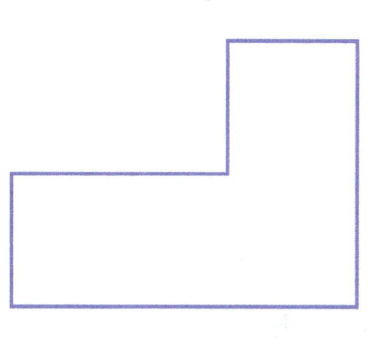 | 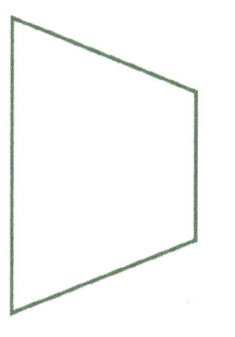 |

2. Which of these shapes are rectangles? Use a postcard or a thin book to help you.

a.

b.       c.

3. Copy the shape in the grid on the right.

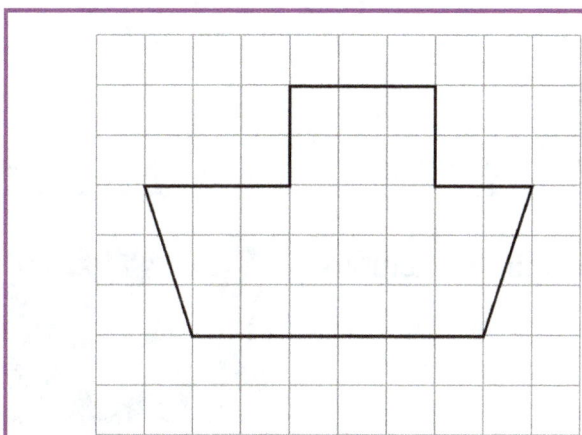
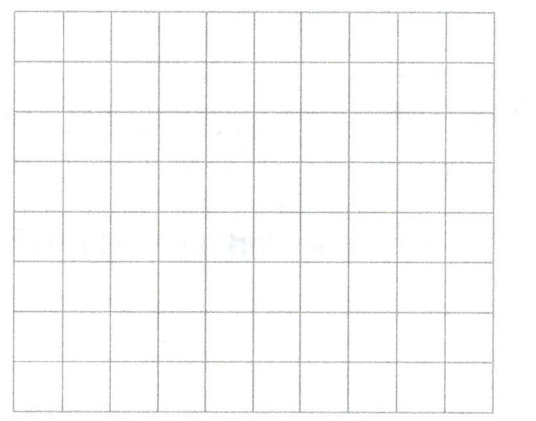

4. Draw a closed shape with straight sides that fits the given rules.
   (Sketching or approximate drawing is sufficient.)

| a.  • The shape has four sides.<br><br>  • Each corner is a "square" corner. | b.  • The shape has three sides.<br><br>  • Two of the sides are the same length. |
|---|---|
|  |  |

5. **Activity.** Use a set of geometric solids. First, build the given shape. Then build a *larger* shape (of your own choice) that has that shape as a part of it.

6. First divide the shape into equal shares, then color.

| **a.** Color 1 half. | **b.** Color 3 quarters. | **c.** Color 2 halves. | **d.** Color 4 fourths. |
|---|---|---|---|
|  |  |  |  |

7. Tell or write how many parts and what kind of parts of the shape are colored.

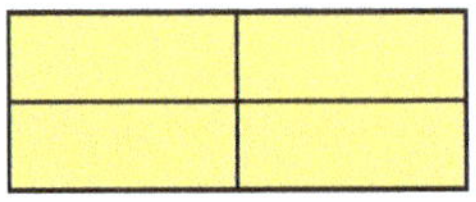

_____  _____ of

the rectangle  are colored.

8. Tell or write what portion of what thing is circled in the picture.

_____ of _____

# Chapter 7: Measurement
## Introduction

This chapter of *Math Mammoth Grade 1* covers the basic concept of measuring (as iterating a measurement unit enough times to match the length of the object), plus measuring length in whole inches and centimeters. The main goal is for the child to understand that measuring length is a process of iterating (repeating) the unit of measure.

Note: If you have the electronic version of this book (a PDF file), you need to print the pages at 100%, instead of using "shrink to fit," "print to fit," or similar options from your printer. Printing with "shrink to fit" will cause the images to be slightly smaller than intended, and thus some exercises about measuring in inches and centimeters will no longer be a whole-number amount of inches or centimeters.

### Good Mathematical Practices

- Measurement gives an opportunity for students to practice being very precise. When using paperclips as measurement units, one needs to lay them in a row very precisely. When using a ruler to measure, it needs positioned precisely, and also needs to be read precisely. Otherwise you will have an error in your measurement.

### Pacing Suggestion for Chapter 7

Please add one day to the pacing for the test if you will use it.

| The Lessons in Chapter 7 | page | span | suggested pacing | your pacing |
|---|---|---|---|---|
| Measuring Length 1 ............................................... | 79 | *2 pages* | 1 day | |
| Measuring Length 2 ............................................... | 81 | *2 pages* | 1 day | |
| Comparing Lengths ............................................... | 83 | *3 pages* | 1 day | |
| Measuring in Inches ............................................. | 86 | *3 pages* | 1 day | |
| Measuring in Centimeters ..................................... | 89 | *2 pages* | 1 day | |
| Chapter 7 Mixed Review ....................................... | 91 | *2 pages* | 1 day | |
| Chapter 7 Review .................................................. | 93 | *1 page* | 1 day | |
| Chapter 7 Test (optional) | | | | |
| TOTALS | | *15 pages* | 7 days | |

# Games and Activities

### Measuring in Inches and Centimeters

The lessons in this chapter contains hands-on measurement activities. Beyond those, you can encourage the child to freely use rulers and measuring tapes around the house or classroom to measure anything and everything.

- Ask the child to find items that are longer than 12 cm (5 inches) but less than 30 cm (12 inches)

- Ask the child to measure their own bed, their own room, and so on.

- Ask the child to measure how tall someone is, by having the person lie down on the floor.

# Games and Activities at Math Mammoth Practice

**Measuring Activity**
Practice measuring the length and height of objects in inches or in centimeters.
https://www.mathmammoth.com/practice/measuring

**Measure Objects in Inches**
Drag the ruler to measure the length or height of different objects in whole inches.
https://www.mathmammoth.com/practice/measuring#q=5&u=2

**Measure Objects in Centimeters.**
Drag the ruler to measure the length or height of different objects in whole centimeters.
https://www.mathmammoth.com/practice/measuring#q=5&u=64

**Measure Objects with a Broken Ruler**
Drag the ruler to measure the length or height of different objects in whole centimeters or inches. This time you need to look at the difference between two points on the ruler, since it does not start at zero.
https://www.mathmammoth.com/practice/measuring#q=10&u=67

## Further Resources on the Internet

We have compiled a list of Internet resources that match the topics in this chapter, including pages that offer:

- **online practice** for concepts;
- online **games**, or occasionally, printable games;
- **animations** and interactive **illustrations** of math concepts;
- **articles** that teach a math concept.

We heartily recommend you take a look! Many of our customers love using these resources to supplement the bookwork. You can use these resources as you see fit for extra practice, to illustrate a concept better and even just for some fun. Enjoy!

https://l.mathmammoth.com/2026/gr1ch7

Scan me

# Measuring Length 1

We measure things to find <u>how long</u> or <u>how wide</u> they are, as compared to other things. For all measuring, we need a **measuring unit**. We repeat the measuring unit many times, and compare it to the thing we are measuring.

1. **Activity.** Measure how long some things are, using a paperclip as a measuring unit.

   <u>You need</u>: Several paperclips that are the same size. Small things to measure, such as an eraser, pencils, crayons, toys, and books.
   The objects being measured should ideally be spanned by a whole number of length units (with no gaps or overlaps).

   But if an object is not exactly a whole number of paperclips, say that the thing is *about* so many paperclips long.

   Measure the length of five things with paperclips:

   _____  _____ paper clips

   _____  _____ paper clips

   _____  _____ paper clips

   _____  _____ paper clips

   _____  _____ paper clips

2. **Activity.** This time we will use a crayon or pencil as a measuring unit.

   <u>You need</u>: Several crayons or pencils that are the same length. Objects to measure, such as books, kitchen utensils, toys, etc. The objects being measured should ideally be spanned by a whole number of length units (with no gaps or overlaps).

   Measure the length of three things with crayons (or pencils):

   _____  _____ crayons

   _____  _____ crayons

   _____  _____ crayons

3. How many crayons long are these pencils?

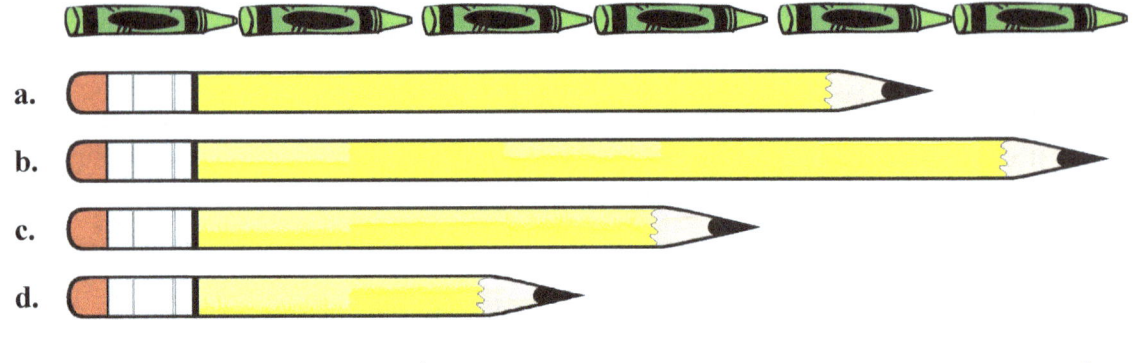

a. _____ crayons long          c. _____ crayons long

b. _____ crayons long          d. _____ crayons long

4. Sarah measured the length of this cucumber using paperclips.

   Do you agree with her result?

   Why or why not?

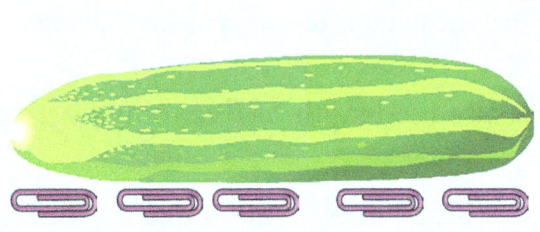

"It is 5 paperclips long."

5. How many paper clips long are the pencils?

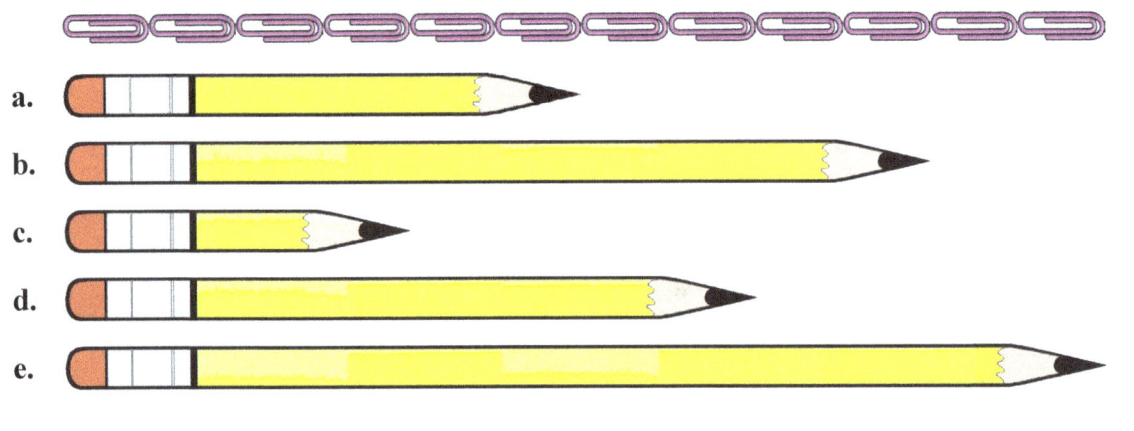

a. _____ paper clips long          d. _____ paper clips long

b. _____ paper clips long          e. _____ paper clips long

c. _____ paper clips long

# Measuring Length 2

1. **Activity.** Order three objects by length.
   <u>You need</u>: Several sets of three objects of unequal length.
   The student will order the three objects by length, from the shortest to the longest.

   Variation: if it is easy, give the student(s) more objects to order by length.

2. Order these things from the shortest to the longest. Write 1 on the shortest object,
   2 on the one that is neither the shortest nor the longest, and 3 on the longest.

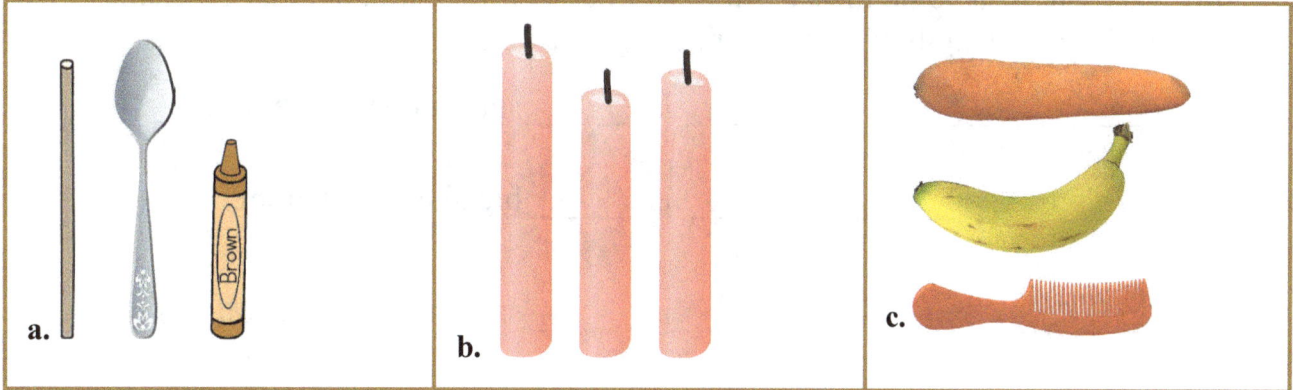

3. Order the crayons from the shortest to the longest, numbering them with 1, 2, 3, and 4.

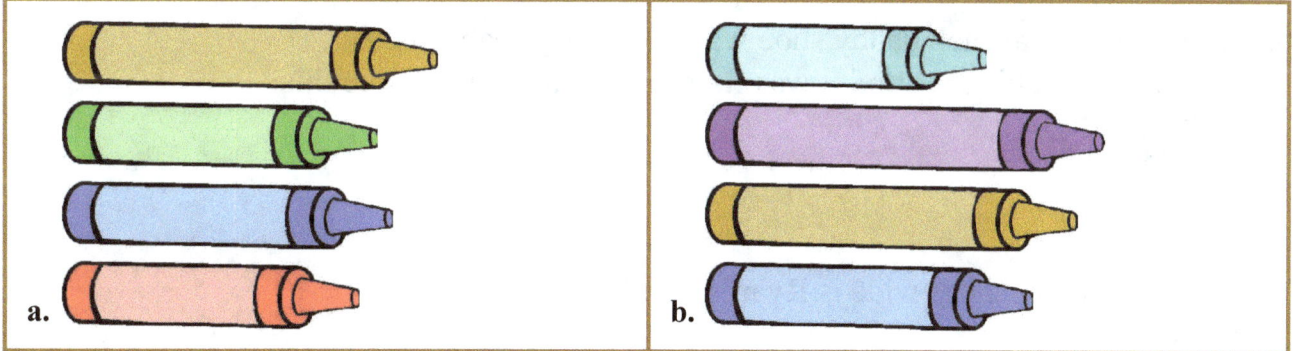

4. Eric used spoons to measure the width of a tabletop. He said it is 7 spoons wide.
   Do you agree with him? If not, explain why. (one spoon = ⌐— )

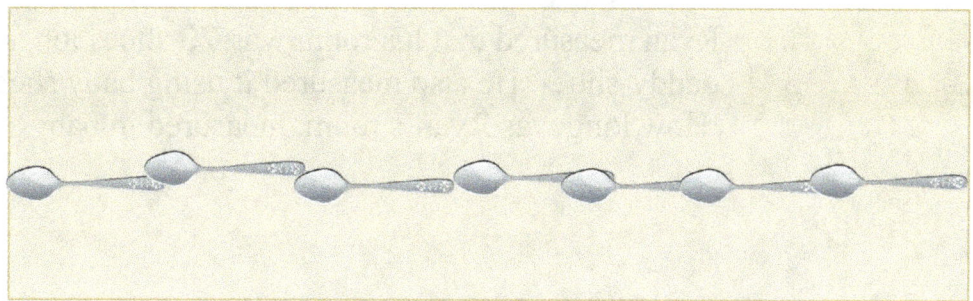

5. **Activity.** (optional) Use two kinds of shoes as measuring units.
   <u>**You need**</u>: two small shoes and two bigger shoes.

   a. Measure a desk or a table. Place one shoe at the edge of the table and the other
      one directly behind it. Then move the first shoe in
      front of the second, and so on. Keep count.

      The table is _____ small shoes wide.

      The table is _____ big shoes wide.

   b. Measure two more things now, using *both* the small shoes and the big shoes.
      For example, you could measure the width of a whiteboard, height of a chair,
      or your friend's length when they are lying on a floor.

      _____ is _____ small shoes wide/long.

      _____ is _____ big shoes wide/long.

      _____ is _____ small shoes wide/long.

      _____ is _____ big shoes wide/long.

6. Ryan noticed that each daddy shoe was about <u>three</u> baby shoes.
   Ryan measured his desk and it was four daddy-shoes wide, like this:

   How many baby-shoes wide is Ryan's desk?
   Hint: Draw.

   **Puzzle Corner**   Ryan measured that his room was 23 shoes long, using
                       daddy-shoes. He also measured it using baby shoes.
                       How long was Ryan's room, measured in baby shoes?

# Comparing Lengths

Sometimes we cannot easily tell which of two things is longer (or wider). We can use a third thing as a "**measuring stick**." Look at these two houses. Can you tell which one is longer?

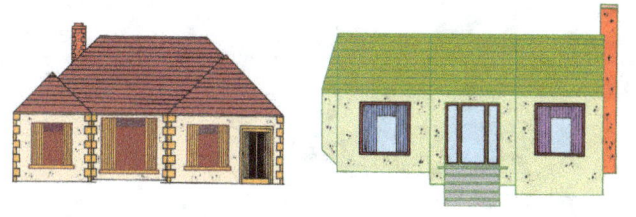

Now let's use a "log" as a measuring stick:

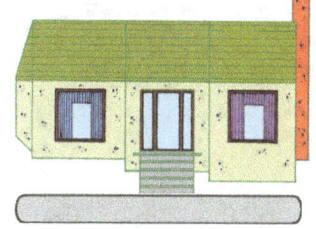

House 1 is a little shorter than our log.        House 2 is a little longer than our log.

Is house 1 longer than house 2? Or the other way around?

House 2 is longer than house 1, because it is longer than our log, whereas house 1 is shorter than the log.

1. **Activity**. Compare lengths of two things using a third object as a "measuring stick."
   You will need: Choose several sets of two objects or things to compare in this manner, and a suitable measuring stick that is shorter than one of the objects but longer than the other object.

   The things to compare should be fairly close in length (or width or height) so that you cannot easily see visually which is longer. Also, do not bring the objects near each other for the same reason. For example, you could compare the width of a window and the width of a desk, with a yardstick or a broom. Or, compare the length of a keyboard with the width of a chair using a clothes hanger. You can also make the measuring stick of just the right length for your situation for example from a pipe cleaner.

   Write down your results for one set of two objects below.

   _____ is shorter than the "measuring stick".

   _____ is shorter than the "measuring stick".

   So, _____ is longer than _____.

2. Compare the things to the "measuring stick." Mark the <u>longer</u> of the two.

a.

b.

c.

d.

3. Cut out (carefully!) the measuring sticks from the bottom of this page and use them to compare the lengths of these things. Use the stick labeled with **a.** for the part (a) the stick **b.** for (b), and the stick **c.** for part (c).

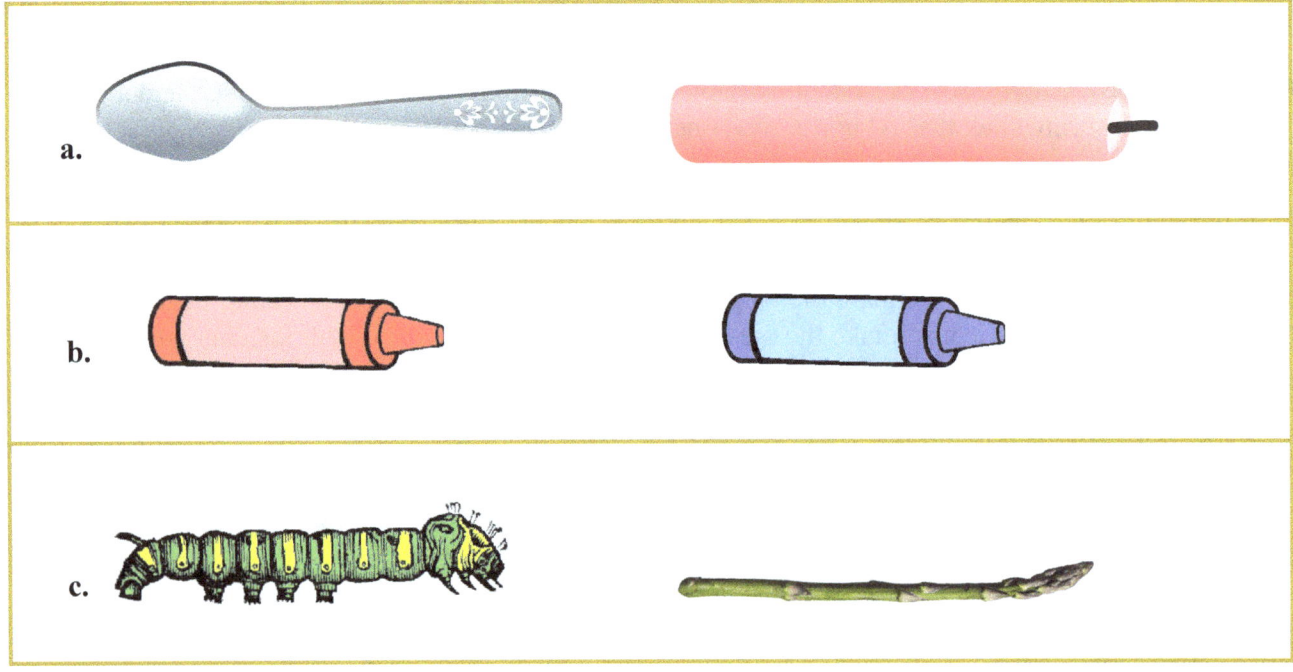

a.

b.

c.

Cut out these:

a.          b.          c.

4. Draw a picture to match the situation. You can draw stick figures.

**a.** Jerry is shorter than the top of the cabinet. The top of the cabinet is shorter than Mike.

**b.** The table is taller than little Kyle. Little Mary is taller than the table.

# Measuring in Inches

This line is 1 inch long. ├────────┤ We also write "1 in." or "1 in" for short.

1. How many inches long are these sticks?

a.  _____ inches

b.  _____ inches

c. _____ in

d.  _____ in

2. Now use the ruler. How many inches long are these items?

a. 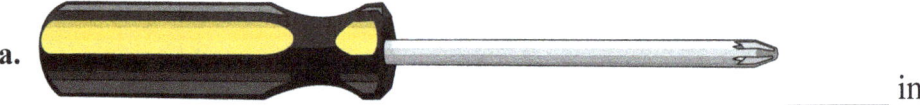 _____ in

b. _____ in

```
|   1   |   2   |   3   |   4   |   5   |   6
```

c. _____ in

d. 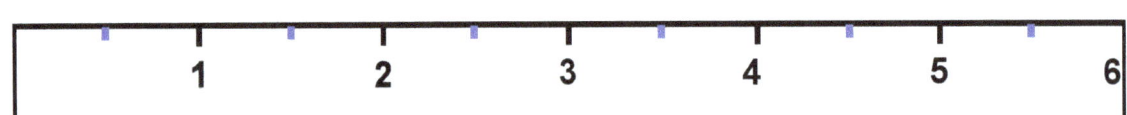 _____ in

```
|   1   |   2   |   3   |   4   |   5   |   6
```

e. 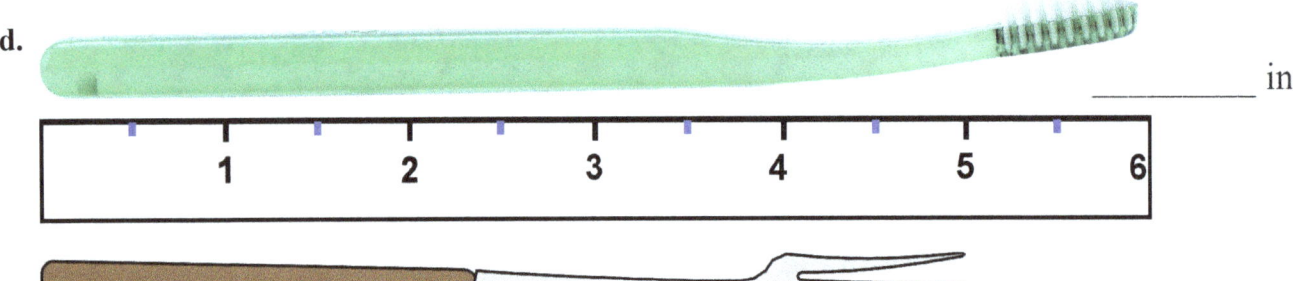 _____ in

3. Measure the lines with a ruler.

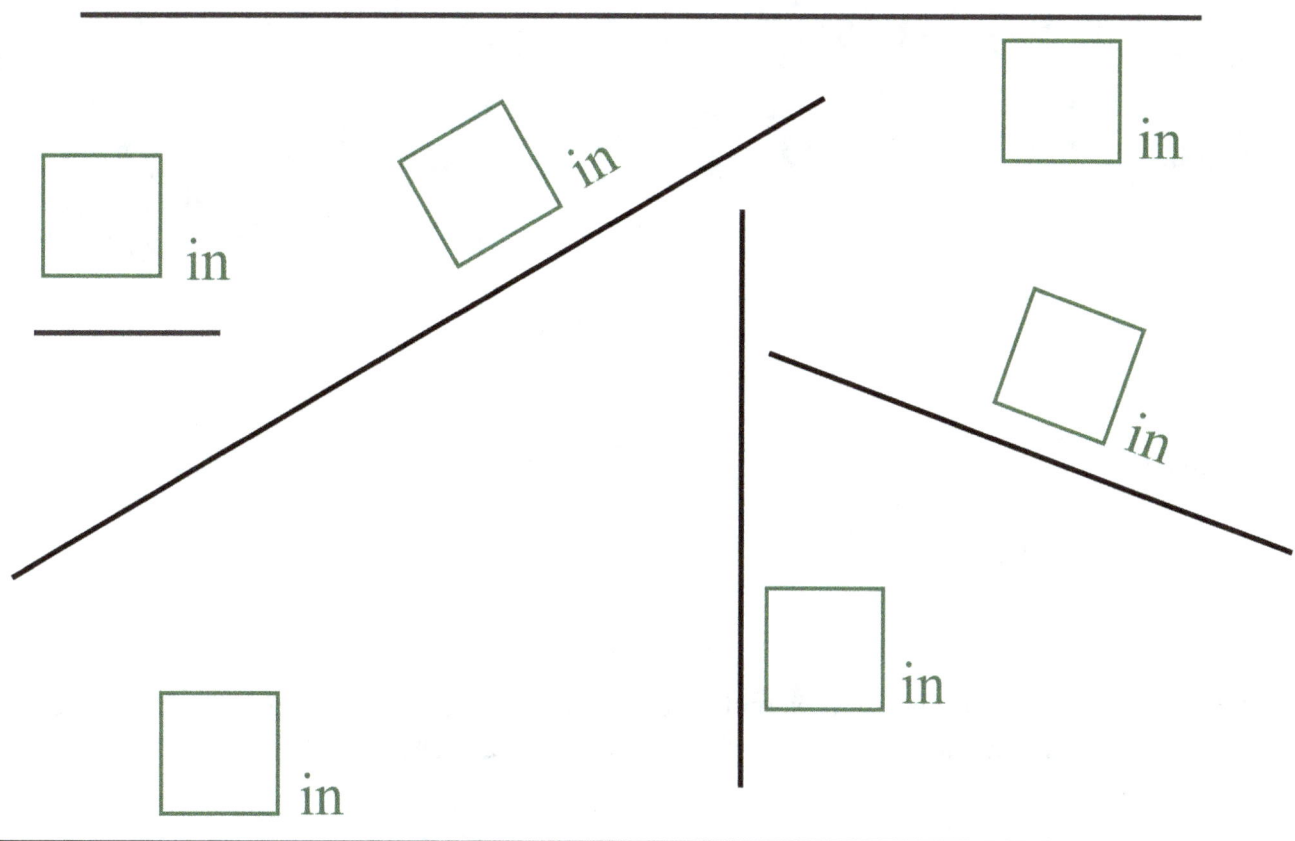

4. Measure the sides of the triangles.

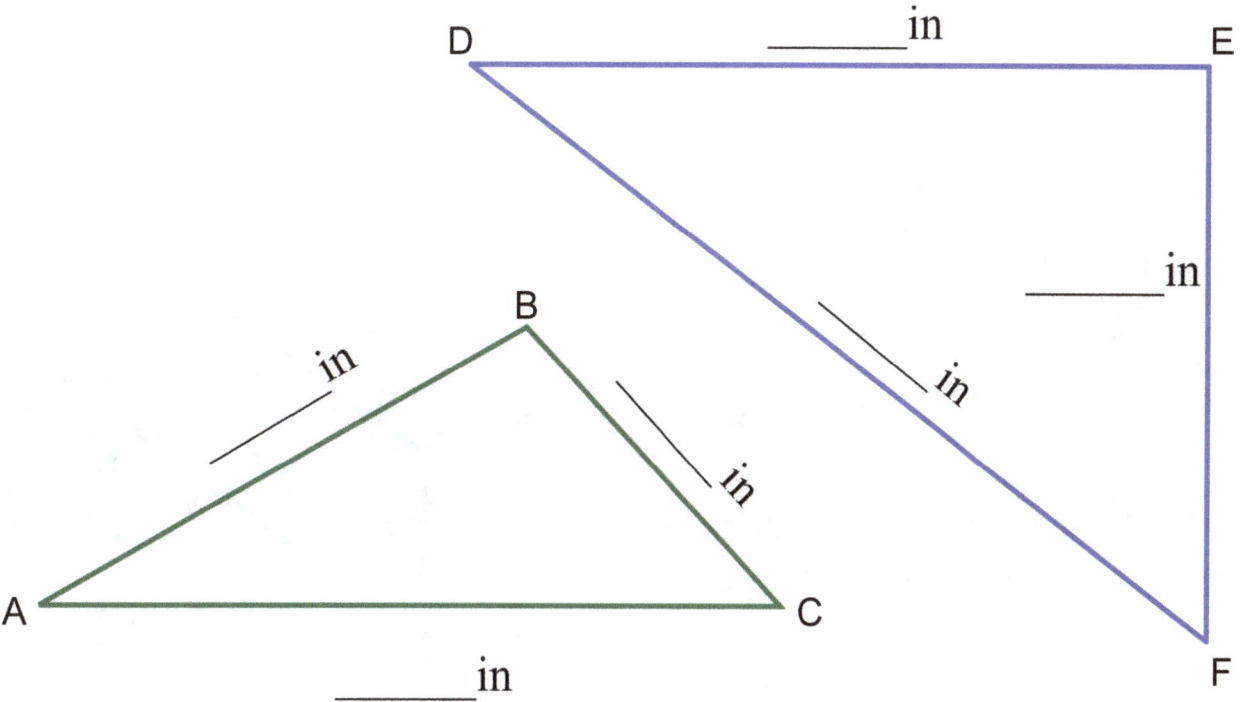

5. Use a ruler and draw lines with these lengths:

**a.** 4 in

**b.** 2 in

**c.** 5 in

**d.** 7 in

**e.** 1 in

**f.** 8 in

6. Draw the last side for these figures with a ruler. Then measure all the sides of each figure. Write the measurement next to each side (for example "2 inches" or "2 in").

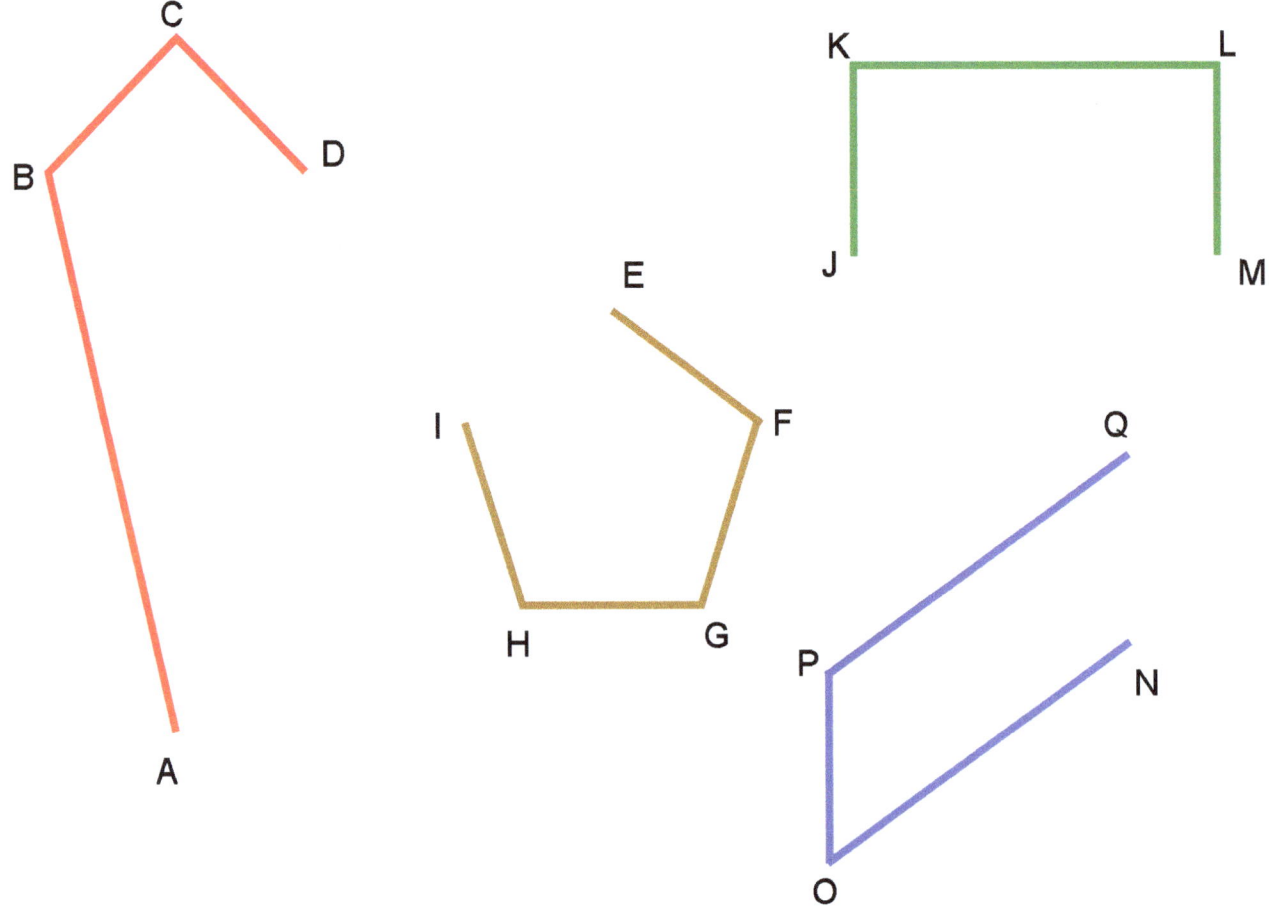

# Measuring in Centimeters

You can find out how long things are in *centimeters*.

This line is 1 centimeter long: ⊢━━┤
A centimeter is written in its short form as "cm."
This pencil is 6 cm long.

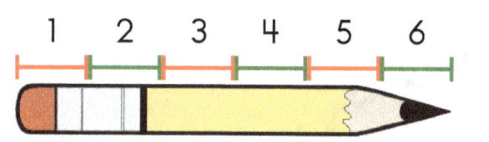

1. How many centimeters long are these things?

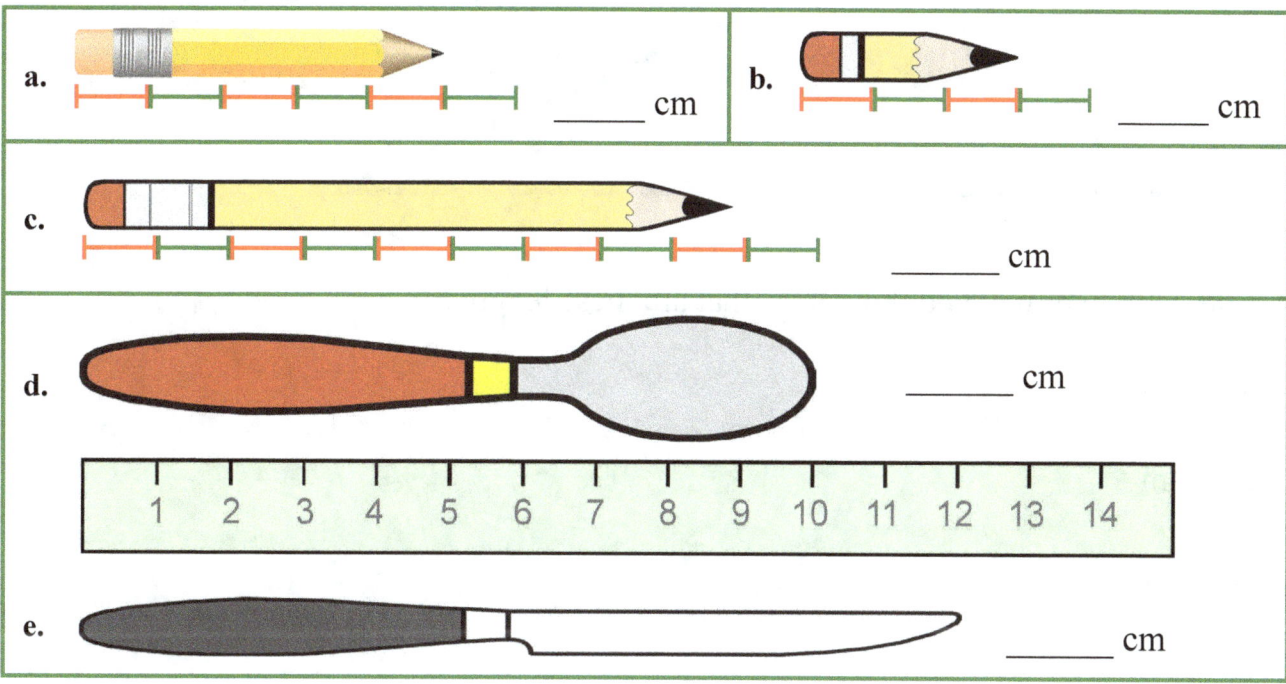

a. _____ cm

b. _____ cm

c. _____ cm

d. _____ cm

e. _____ cm

2. Measure the lines with a ruler. (If you don't have one, cut out the ruler at the bottom of the page.)

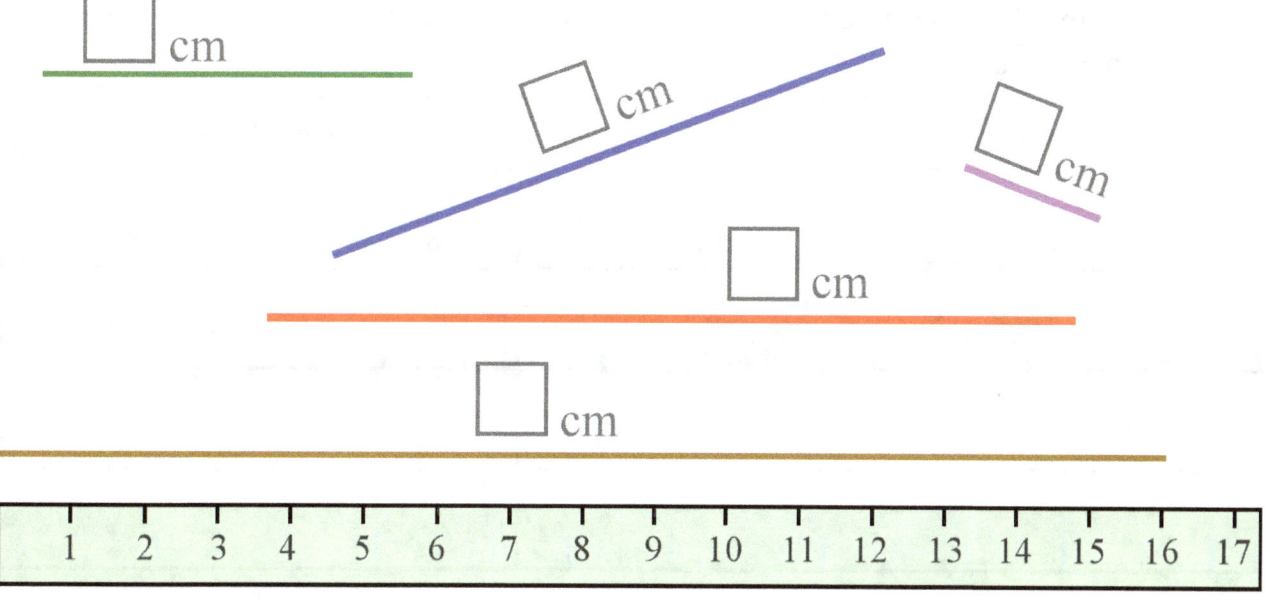

☐ cm

☐ cm

☐ cm

☐ cm

☐ cm

3. Draw the last side for these figures with a ruler. Then measure all three sides of each figure. Write the measurement next to each line (for example "6 cm").

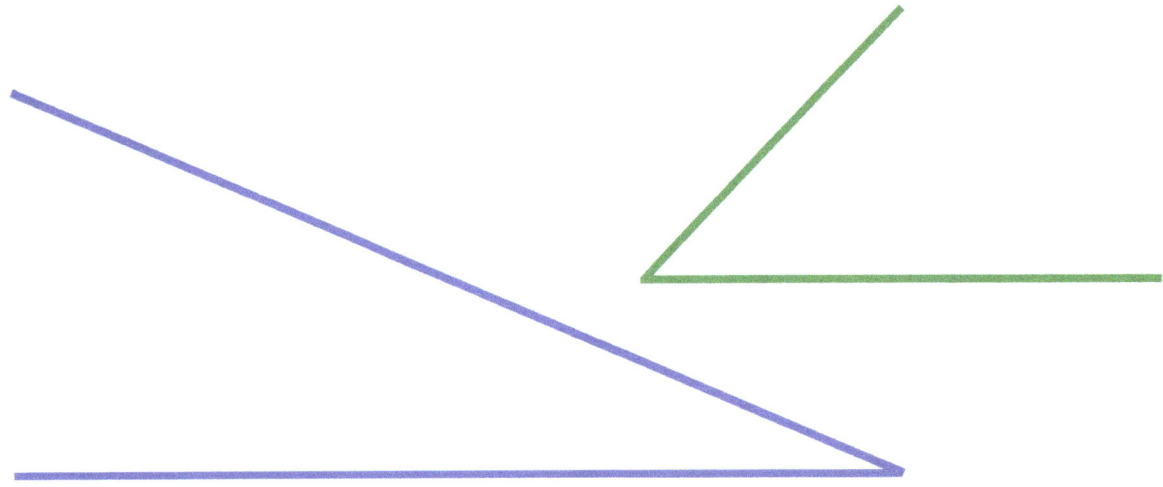

4. Use your own ruler and draw lines that are these lengths.

   **a.** 4 cm

   **b.** 5 cm

   **c.** 8 cm

   **d.** 16 cm

5. Measure some things around you in centimeters! For example, a book, your pencil, a table, and so on.

| Thing | How long? |
|---|---|
|  |  |
|  |  |
|  |  |
|  |  |

# Chapter 7 Mixed Review

1. Add and subtract 10.

| | | |
|---|---|---|
| **a.** $45 + 10 =$ _____<br><br>$45 - 10 =$ _____ | **b.** $88 + 10 =$ _____<br><br>$88 - 10 =$ _____ | **c.** $100 + 10 =$ _____<br><br>$100 - 10 =$ _____ |
| **d.** $8 + 10 =$ _____ | **e.** $14 - 10 =$ _____ | **f.** $90 + 10 =$ _____ |

2. Complete the fact families with 7.

**a.**

$2 \ + \ $ _____ $ = 7$

_____ $ + \ $ _____ $ = 7$

$7 - \ $ _____ $ = \ $ _____

$7 - \ $ _____ $ = \ $ _____

**b.**

_____ $ + \ $ _____ $ = 7$

_____ $ + \ $ _____ $ = 7$

$7 - \ $ _____ $ = \ 3$

$7 - \ $ _____ $ = \ $ _____

3. Solve. Write an addition or a subtraction equation for each problem.
   Write either + or − symbol in the gray box.

**a.** Avery's family has two dogs. But then they got six puppies! How many dogs does the family have now?

_____ ☐ _____ = _____

They have _____ dogs now.

**b.** Sam's cat had seven kittens last year. This year, the cat again had kittens, but two fewer than last year. How many kittens did it have this year?

_____ ☐ _____ = _____

The cat had _____ kittens this year.

4. Fill in the missing numbers, thinking of fact families.

| a. | b. | c. | d. |
|---|---|---|---|
| $0 + \underline{\hphantom{XX}} = 8$ | $5 + \underline{\hphantom{XX}} = 9$ | $6 - \underline{\hphantom{XX}} = 4$ | $10 - \underline{\hphantom{XX}} = 5$ |
| $2 + \underline{\hphantom{XX}} = 8$ | $3 + \underline{\hphantom{XX}} = 9$ | $6 - \underline{\hphantom{XX}} = 3$ | $10 - \underline{\hphantom{XX}} = 8$ |
| $5 + \underline{\hphantom{XX}} = 8$ | $2 + \underline{\hphantom{XX}} = 9$ | $6 - \underline{\hphantom{XX}} = 1$ | $10 - \underline{\hphantom{XX}} = 3$ |
| $4 + \underline{\hphantom{XX}} = 8$ | $1 + \underline{\hphantom{XX}} = 9$ | $6 - \underline{\hphantom{XX}} = 6$ | $10 - \underline{\hphantom{XX}} = 6$ |

5. Draw a closed shape with straight sides that fits the given rules.
   (Sketching or approximate drawing is sufficient.)

| | |
|---|---|
| **a.** • The shape has four sides.<br>• Each corner is a "square" corner. | **b.** • The shape has three sides.<br>• Two of the sides are the same length. |
| **c.** • The shape has six sides. | **d.** • The shape has four sides.<br>• Each corner is a "square" corner.<br>• Each side is the same length. |

6. (optional) Your teacher will give you a calendar. What day of the week is...

**a.** February 7 _____   **b.** April 22 _____

**c.** August 11 _____   **d.** today _____

# Chapter 7 Review

1. **Activity.** Measure both the width and the length of a desk (or a table) using spoons.
   <u>You need</u>: Several identical small spoons, preferably fairly short (teaspoons).

   The student will use the spoons to measure the width and length of a desk or table.
   If the desk is not exactly so many spoons wide (long), indicate the length using
   "between" or "about", such as "between 8 and 9 spoons," or "about 8 spoons."

2. Order the crayons from the shortest to the longest, numbering them with 1, 2, and 3.

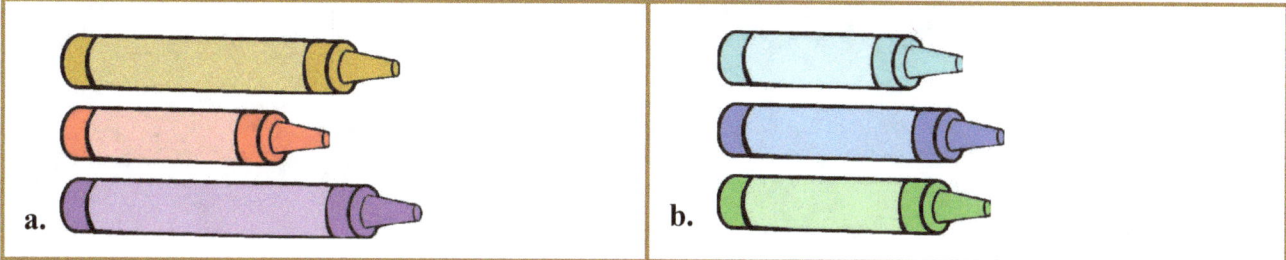

a.    b.

3. How many corners does this shape have?

   (We call it a *pentagon*.)

   Measure its sides in centimeters.
   Write each length next to the side.

4. Measure with an inch-ruler.

   a.    _____ in

   b.                                    _____ in

5. Cut out (carefully!) the measuring stick from the bottom of this page and use it
   to compare the lengths of these things. Is the spoon or the toothbrush longer?

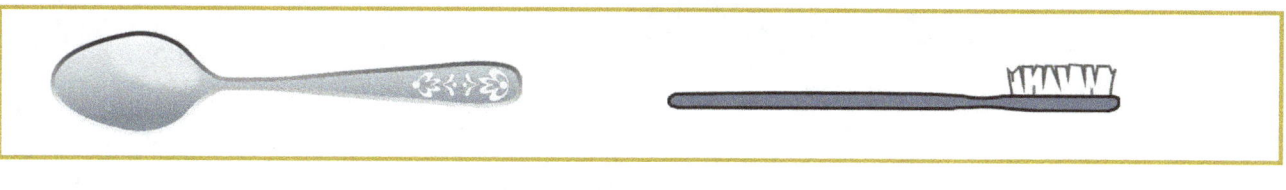

   Cut out:

# Chapter 8: Adding and Subtracting Within 0-100
## Introduction

This chapter deals with two major topics: adding and subtracting within 0-20 and adding and subtracting two-digit numbers. These two major topics are blended together in a somewhat spiral manner. The subtopics include:

- Adding a two-digit number and a single-digit number without regrouping (carrying) (for example, 23 + 4 or 56 + 3).

- Subtracting a one-digit number from a two-digit number without regrouping (borrowing): For example, 45 − 3 or 67 − 6.

- Adding and subtracting two-digit numbers in columns (one number under the other) without regrouping.

- Recognizing that sometimes in adding two-digit numbers we need to regroup — to combine ten ones to make a new ten. In this grade level, we approach this concept mainly using visual models. Children are also welcome to use the 100-bead abacus to solve these problems. The standard algorithm where one number is written under the other will be studied in 2nd grade.

- Learning specific mental math strategies for adding and subtracting numbers under 20 (such as 7 + 9 or 15 − 8). We study a trick with nine and eight, adding just one more than a known sum, and using the relationship between addition and subtraction to subtract.

Please note that while the chapter includes several basic strategies for adding and subtracting within 0-20, the goal is not to memorize the basic addition where the sum is between 11 and 18, and the corresponding subtraction facts. That will happen in 2nd grade. Right now, the idea is to build the student's **number sense**: the ability to manipulate numbers by breaking them apart and composing them in different ways.

Also in second grade, your child or students will learn the traditional paper-and-pencil algorithms of adding and subtracting in columns. They will also learn more mental math. This means they will be able to fluently add and subtract numbers within 0-100. They will also learn to add and subtract three-digit numbers.

**Good Mathematical Practices**

- Mental math strategies allow your child or students to observe patterns inherent in our base-ten number system. For example, knowing that 8 + 7 = 15 allows one to easily add 28 + 7. Or, there is a similarity in the subtractions 10 − 4, 50 − 4, and 80 − 4. This is what good number sense is all about: being able to recognize these patterns and structures, and to use them to do calculations in one's head.

- Several lessons in the chapter ask the child to write an equation (a calculation) for a situation in a word problem. This is the very beginning stage of modeling with mathematics: applying mathematics to solve problems arising in everyday life.


## Pacing Suggestion for Chapter 8

Please add one day to the pacing for the test if you will use it.

| The Lessons in Chapter 8 | page | span | suggested pacing | your pacing |
|---|---|---|---|---|
| Some Old, Some New | 100 | *2 pages* | 1 day | |
| Add Using "Just One More" | 102 | *2 pages* | 1 day | |
| A "Trick" with Nine | 104 | *2 pages* | 1 day | |
| A "Trick" with Eight | 106 | *2 pages* | 1 day | |
| Add a Two-Digit and a Single-Digit Number | 108 | *2 pages* | 1 day | |

## Math Talks

A friendly reminder: try to have some "math talks" from time to time with your student(s) using photos from https://www.mathmammoth.com/MathTalks plus using objects and scenes you see in your life!

# Games and Activities

### Pyramid Solitaire

**You need:** A deck of number cards with numbers up to the target number. You can play Pyramid with target numbers 13, 12, 11, 10, and so on.

**Game play:** Let's say the target number is 13. Deal 21 cards in six rows, in the shape of a pyramid, so that the first row has 1 card, the second row has 2, the third row has 3, and so on. The cards need to overlap. See the illustration. The rest of the cards stay in a deck, face down.

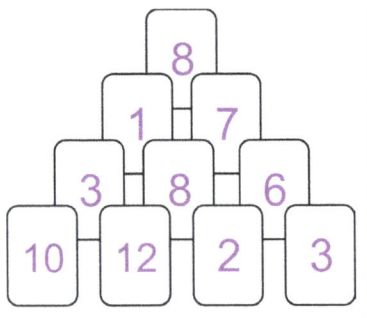

You can remove from the pyramid any two cards that add up to the target number and that are free; in other words, no other cards are partially covering them. In the illustration, though it has only four rows, the cards 10 and 3 could be removed (if the target number is the default 13).

Once you cannot remove any cards from the pyramid, start going through the cards in the deck, one by one, placing each card from the main deck into a discard deck which is face up. You can also remove a card from the pyramid using one of these cards as its pair (so the two add up to the target number).

Once you've gone through the deck, flip it and start over. You can go through the deck as many times as you want.

You win if you can remove all the cards from the pyramid.

**Addition Challenge**

**You need:** A deck of number cards from 3 to 10 (or from 3 to 13). A standard deck of playing cards works fine — just remove the cards that are not needed.

**Game Play:** In each round, each player is dealt two cards face up, and has to calculate their sum. The player with the highest sum gets all the cards from the other players. After enough rounds have been played to use all of the cards, the player with the most cards wins. If two or more players have the same sum, then those players get an additional two cards and use those to resolve the tie.

**11 Out** (or *12 Out* or *13 Out*)

**You need:** A deck of number cards. Regular playing cards work if you let Jack = 11, Queen = 12, and King = 13.

**Preparation:** Choose a target sum, such as 12. Deal seven cards to each player. Place the rest face down in a pile in the middle of the table.

**Game play:** On your turn, first take one card from the pile. Then try to find pairs of cards in your hand that add up to 12, and discard any such pairs. Discard the card 12 (Queen) also if you have it. If you cannot find any such pairs, ask for any one card you want (such as 6) from the player to your right (as in "Go Fish"). That player, if he has it, must give it, and you will then discard the pair that makes 12. Then it is the next player's turn. The player who first discards all the cards from his hand is the winner.

**Variations:**
* Deal more than seven cards.
* Deal fewer cards if there are a lot of players or the players are very young.
* Allow players to discard *three* cards that add up to 12.

**Closest to 11**

**You need:** For the target number of 11, use a deck of number cards from 2 to 9. For the target number of 12, use number cards from 2 to 10. For 13, use cards from 2 to 11 (Jack = 11). And so on.

**Game play:** Choose a target number (from 11 to 16). Each round starts by dealing three times as many cards as there are players, face down on the table. For example, for three players, deal nine cards. The first player chooses three of those cards and turns them over. They will then choose two *or* three of those cards to add, trying to get as close to the target number as possible.

They will take the two or three cards they use to get the sum. If they only use two cards, the third card is left on the table, face up.

The next player now chooses three cards from those on the table (whether face up or down), and again makes a sum, trying to get as close as possible to the target number. They keep the cards they used for the sum. Again, if they only use two cards, the third card is left face up on the table.

At the end of the round, check everyone's sums. The player closest to the target (whether more or less than the target) wins a point. If several players are equally far from the target sum, they all get a point.

Have a number line handy to use for discussions about which player is closer to the target sum.

**Variation:** Use subtraction instead, in which case you would use a lower target number.

*This game is adapted from https://www.earlyfamilymath.org and published here with permission.*

## 21 Card Game

**You need:** A deck of regular playing cards. Each of the face cards counts as 10, and the ace is either 1 or 11 (player's choice at the time of play).

**Game play:** Choose one person to be a dealer. The dealer will deal two cards to each player, face up, and to themselves, one card face up and second card face down. Each player will find the sum of their two cards, and then decide if they want more card(s). The goal is to get to 21, or as close to it as you can without going over. Note that an ace and a face card or 10 makes 21, the perfect score.

The dealer will ask each player, one at a time, if they want one more card, and if yes, they deal it to the player. Upon receiving the third card, the player may choose to get a fourth card, also. If a player now goes over 21, they go bust and have lost. Otherwise, it is the next player's turn to possibly receive more cards.

Here, the player has
gone "bust" because the
total is 10 + 7 + 5 = 22.

This is either 11 + 10 or 1 + 10.
Naturally, you'd want it to be
11 + 10 = 21

After checking with each player whether they want more cards, the dealer also decides the same for himself, and possibly gets a third and a fourth card.

The winner is the player whose sum is closest to 21. Ties are fairly likely!

**Variation 1:** Use number cards from 1 to 13 (e.g. regular playing cards *without* making the face cards to be 10), and have the target sum to be 31 instead of 21. Again, an ace can be either 1 or 11 (player's choice).

**Variation 2:** Instead of the player who is closest to 21 being the winner, each player can play against the dealer, like in Blackjack. However, doing it the way explained above brings in an additional math concept of comparing several numbers.

## Race to 50

**You need:** A large set of number cards from 1-10. For example, you can use the cards from two standard decks of playing cards. A marker for each player. Download the game board from here:
https://www.mathmammoth.com/download/Race-50.pdf

**Game Play:** Deal four cards to each player and place the remaining deck face down on the table. Each player places their marker on START, which signifies zero. On their turn, a player uses their cards to advance on the game board to the next number on their path. They either use a single card or add several of the numbers together.

For example, to advance from START to the circle with 11, the player could use 4 & 7, placing those cards in the discard pile. If a player cannot go, they will draw one card from the deck, and it is the next player's turn.

If the player has less than four cards in their hand after their turn, they will draw enough cards from the pile to again have four cards.

The winner is the player who reaches the middle number (50) first.

# Games and Activities at Math Mammoth Practice

**Hidden Picture Addition Game**
Use a number range of 3 to 19, or some other, to practice addition.
https://www.mathmammoth.com/practice/mystery-picture

**Hidden Picture Subtraction Game**
Choose a number range of 2 to 18, for example, to practice subtraction in this fun game.
https://www.mathmammoth.com/practice/mystery-picture-subtraction

**Bingo**
Choose Addition (Single-Digit).
https://www.mathmammoth.com/practice/bingo

**Mathy's Berry Picking Adventure**
Join Mathy (our mammoth mascot) on his berry-picking adventure, and practice your mental math! The link below gives you addition and subtraction problems within 0-20.
https://www.mathmammoth.com/practice/mathy-berries#mode=addition-single&duration=2m

**Make Addition Sentences**
You're given numbers (in flowers), and an answer to an addition. Drag two flowers to the empty slots so that the addition is true.
https://www.mathmammoth.com/practice/number-sentences#questions=10&types=add-1-20

**Two-Digit Mental Addition - Online Practice**
Practice adding one two-digit number and one single-digit number without regrouping in this online quiz.
https://www.mathmammoth.com/practice/addition-subtraction-two-digit#opts=2p1dnr

**Two-Digit Mental Subtraction - Online Practice**
Practice subtracting a single-digit number from a two-digit number without regrouping in this online quiz.
https://www.mathmammoth.com/practice/addition-subtraction-two-digit#opts=2m1dnr

**Fruity Math**
Click the fruit with the correct answer and try to get as many points as you can in the allotted time.
You could start with Level 1, in which case the game will automatically advance towards harder problems, or you could use the "Manual" setting to choose the exact types of numbers to add.
https://www.mathmammoth.com/practice/fruity-math

## Further Resources on the Internet

We have compiled a list of Internet resources that match the topics in this chapter, including pages that offer:

- **online practice** for concepts;
- online **games**, or occasionally, printable games;
- **animations** and interactive **illustrations** of math concepts;
- **articles** that teach a math concept.

Scan me

We heartily recommend you take a look! Many of our customers love using these resources to supplement the bookwork. You can use these resources as you see fit for extra practice, to illustrate a concept better and even just for some fun. Enjoy!

https://l.mathmammoth.com/2026/gr1ch8

# Some Old, Some New

1. Decompose (break up) the numbers into two parts.

| 7 | 8 | 9 | 10 |
|---|---|---|---|
| 5 and _____ | 1 and _____ | 4 and _____ | 3 and _____ |
| 6 and _____ | 4 and _____ | 8 and _____ | 9 and _____ |
| 1 and _____ | 5 and _____ | 2 and _____ | 6 and _____ |
| 2 and _____ | 7 and _____ | 1 and _____ | 5 and _____ |
| 4 and _____ | 2 and _____ | 3 and _____ | 2 and _____ |

2. Count forwards or backwards to add or subtract. The number line can help.

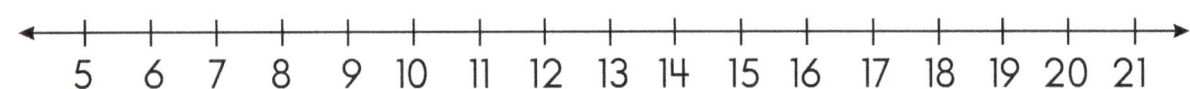

| a. | b. | c. |
|---|---|---|
| $17 + 2 =$ _____ | $13 + 1 + 1 =$ _____ | $9 + 2 + 2 =$ _____ |
| $14 - 2 =$ _____ | $15 - 1 - 2 =$ _____ | $12 - 2 - 2 =$ _____ |

3. Add or subtract.

| | | |
|---|---|---|
| a. $20 + 6 =$ _____ | b. $30 + 40 =$ _____ | c. $50 - 20 =$ _____ |
| $40 + 8 =$ _____ | $80 + 20 =$ _____ | $100 - 90 =$ _____ |
| d. $2 + 50 =$ _____ | e. $32 + 10 =$ _____ | f. $66 - 10 =$ _____ |
| $100 + 7 =$ _____ | $67 + 10 =$ _____ | $82 - 10 =$ _____ |

## A trick (or a shortcut)!

When adding several numbers, look for number that make 10, and add those first.

| **Example 1.** | **Example 2.** |
|---|---|
| 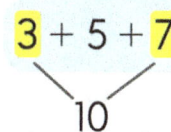 | 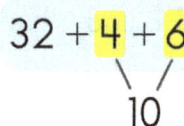 |
| Add 3 and 7 first, to make 10. The sum then becomes 10 + 5. And that equals 15. | We can add 4 and 6 first, to get 10. The sum becomes 32 + 10 which equals 42. |

4. Add.

| **a.** | **b.** | **c.** |
|---|---|---|
| $5 + 5 + 5 = \underline{\hspace{1.5cm}}$ | $6 + 4 + 8 = \underline{\hspace{1.5cm}}$ | $8 + 30 + 2 = \underline{\hspace{1.5cm}}$ |
| $2 + 7 + 8 = \underline{\hspace{1.5cm}}$ | $7 + 2 + 2 = \underline{\hspace{1.5cm}}$ | $45 + 3 + 7 = \underline{\hspace{1.5cm}}$ |
| **d.** | **e.** | **f.** |
| $1 + 31 + 9 = \underline{\hspace{1.5cm}}$ | $5 + 4 + 1 = \underline{\hspace{1.5cm}}$ | $13 + 1 + 9 = \underline{\hspace{1.5cm}}$ |
| $5 + 62 + 5 = \underline{\hspace{1.5cm}}$ | $4 + 3 + 7 = \underline{\hspace{1.5cm}}$ | $4 + 90 + 6 = \underline{\hspace{1.5cm}}$ |

5. Add and subtract. Start with the number in the bottom left corner and follow the arrows.

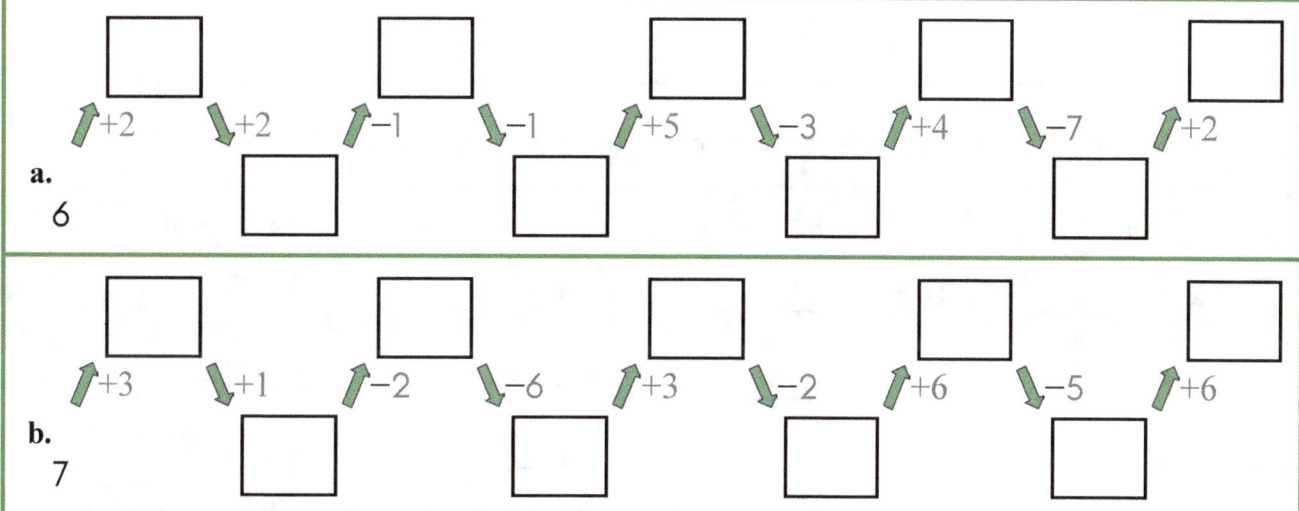

101

# Add Using "Just One More"

Do you remember the numbers that add up to 10 ("the sums of 10")?
There are 9 and 1, and what others? List them now:

**JUST ONE MORE than a sum of 10:**

| | | | |
|---|---|---|---|
| $8 + \underline{2} = 10$ | $8 + 3$ is JUST ONE MORE than $8 + 2$, so the answer | $\underline{5} + 5 = 10$ | $6 + 5$ is JUST ONE MORE than $5 + 5$, so the answer |
| $8 + \underline{3} = 11$ | is also just one more. | $\underline{6} + 5 = 11$ | is also just one more. |

1. Change the underlined number to be JUST ONE MORE. The answer changes, too!

| | | |
|---|---|---|
| **a.** $8 + \underline{\ 2\ } = 10$  $8 + \underline{\ 3\ } = \underline{\quad}$ | **b.** $4 + \underline{\ 6\ } = 10$  $4 + \underline{\quad} = \underline{\quad}$ | **c.** $\underline{\ 7\ } + 3 = 10$  $\underline{\quad} + 3 = \underline{\quad}$ |
| **d.** $\underline{1} + 9 = 10$  $\underline{\quad} + 9 = \underline{\quad}$ | **e.** $5 + \underline{\ 5\ } = 10$  $5 + \underline{\quad} = \underline{\quad}$ | **f.** $\underline{\ 4\ } + 4 = 8$  $\underline{\quad} + 4 = \underline{\quad}$ |

2. Fill in the missing numbers.

| | | |
|---|---|---|
| **a.** $7 + \boxed{\phantom{0}} = 10$  $7 + \boxed{\phantom{0}} = 11$ | **b.** $8 + \boxed{\phantom{0}} = 10$  $8 + \boxed{\phantom{0}} = 11$ | **c.** $6 + \boxed{\phantom{0}} = 10$  $6 + \boxed{\phantom{0}} = 11$ |

3. Add. Color the problems where the sum is just one more than 10.

| a. | b. | c. | d. |
|---|---|---|---|
| $7 + 2 = \underline{\quad}$ | $5 + 6 = \underline{\quad}$ | $4 + 6 = \underline{\quad}$ | $2 + 9 = \underline{\quad}$ |
| $3 + 8 = \underline{\quad}$ | $3 + 4 = \underline{\quad}$ | $2 + 8 = \underline{\quad}$ | $5 + 4 = \underline{\quad}$ |
| $5 + 5 = \underline{\quad}$ | $6 + 4 = \underline{\quad}$ | $7 + 4 = \underline{\quad}$ | $3 + 7 = \underline{\quad}$ |

The **double** of something means twice (two times) that thing.
For example, "double four" means 4 and 4. So double 4 is 8.

4. Fill in the **doubles chart** and notice the pattern it has.

| | |
|---|---|
| $1 + 1 =$ _____ | $6 + 6 =$ _____ |
| $2 + 2 =$ _____ | $7 + 7 =$ 14 |
| $3 + 3 =$ _____ | $8 + 8 =$ _____ |
| $4 + 4 =$ _____ | $9 + 9 =$ 18 |
| $5 + 5 =$ _____ | $10 + 10 =$ _____ |

5. Add. Under each doubles fact, write the sum that is just one more.

| | | |
|---|---|---|
| **a.** $8 + 8 =$ _____ <br><br> $8 + \underline{9} =$ _____ | **b.** $6 + 6 =$ _____ <br><br> $6 +$ ____ $=$ _____ | **c.** $5 + 5 =$ _____ <br><br> $5 +$ ____ $=$ _____ |
| **d.** $7 + 7 =$ _____ <br><br> $7 +$ ____ $=$ _____ | **e.** $4 + 4 =$ _____ <br><br> $4 +$ ____ $=$ _____ | **f.** $9 + 9 =$ _____ <br><br> $9 +$ ____ $=$ _____ |

6. Solve.

Carter bought a package of 12 balloons. He gave three to Mason, two to his sister and five to Mila. How many balloons did he give away?

How many balloons does Carter have left?

7. Add three numbers. Look for numbers that add to 10.

| **a.** | **b.** | **c.** |
|---|---|---|
| $2 + 90 + 8 =$ _____ | $4 + 4 + 3 =$ _____ | $1 + 12 + 9 =$ _____ |
| $3 + 7 + 6 =$ _____ | $4 + 2 + 6 =$ _____ | $2 + 110 + 8 =$ _____ |

# A "Trick" with Nine

Imagine that nine wants to be ten! He is not happy—he wants to become a full TEN! So, nine asks the other number (this time, seven) to give him one in order to make him a ten.

Seven says, "Okay," gives one to nine, and has only six left for himself. In the end, we have 10 and 6. We get 16.

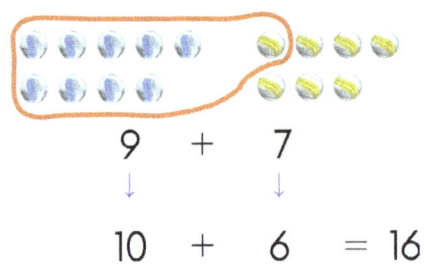

$$9 + 7$$
$$\downarrow \qquad \downarrow$$
$$10 + 6 = 16$$

We can also show the same thing this way →

$$9 + 7$$
$$9 + 1 + 6$$
$$10 + 6 = 16$$

1. Circle all of the blue marbles and enough of the yellow ones to make a ten. Add.

a. $9 + 6$
$\downarrow \qquad \downarrow$
$10 + \underline{5} = \underline{\phantom{00}}$

b. $9 + 4$
$\downarrow \qquad \downarrow$
$10 + \underline{\phantom{0}} = \underline{\phantom{00}}$

c. $9 + 3$
$\downarrow \qquad \downarrow$
$10 + \underline{\phantom{0}} = \underline{\phantom{00}}$

d. $9 + 5$
$\downarrow \qquad \downarrow$
$10 + \underline{\phantom{0}} = \underline{\phantom{00}}$

2. Fill in the blanks. Imagine that nine wants to become a ten.

a. $9 + 6$
$9 + \underline{\phantom{0}} + \underline{\phantom{0}}$
$10 + \underline{\phantom{0}} = \underline{\phantom{00}}$

b. $9 + 7$
$9 + \underline{\phantom{0}} + \underline{\phantom{0}}$
$10 + \underline{\phantom{0}} = \underline{\phantom{00}}$

3. Fill in the blanks. Imagine that nine wants to become a ten.

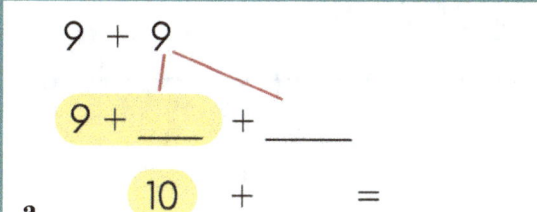

a.
$9 + 9$
$9 + \underline{\quad} + \underline{\quad}$
$10 + \underline{\quad} = \underline{\quad}$

b.
$9 + 4$
$9 + \underline{\quad} + \underline{\quad}$
$10 + \underline{\quad} = \underline{\quad}$

4. How about if the second number is 9, such as $5 + 9$?
   Can you use the trick with 9 in that case? Explain.

5. Solve.

a. A basket had nine apples in it. Aaliyah ate two,
   and her brother ate one. How many apples are left?

b. Alice picked 7 flowers and Oliver picked 9.
   How many more flowers did Oliver pick than Alice?

   How many flowers did the children pick altogether?

6. Fill in the doubles chart again.

| | |
|---|---|
| $1 + 1 = \underline{\quad}$ | $6 + 6 = \underline{\quad}$ |
| $2 + 2 = \underline{\quad}$ | $7 + 7 = \underline{\quad}$ |
| $3 + 3 = \underline{\quad}$ | $8 + 8 = \underline{\quad}$ |
| $4 + 4 = \underline{\quad}$ | $9 + 9 = \underline{\quad}$ |
| $5 + 5 = \underline{\quad}$ | $10 + 10 = \underline{\quad}$ |

7. Add. Use the trick with nine or
   "just one more" than a double.

a. $5 + 6 = \underline{\quad}$

b. $9 + 8 = \underline{\quad}$

c. $2 + 9 = \underline{\quad}$

d. $7 + 8 = \underline{\quad}$

e. $6 + 7 = \underline{\quad}$

8. Right or not? Correct the equations that are *false*.

a. $6 + 6 = 13$      b. $12 = 4 + 9$      c. $9 + 6 = 15$      d. $17 = 9 + 7$

# A "Trick" with Eight

Imagine that eight wants to be ten! She's not happy—she wants to become a full TEN!
So eight asks the other number (this time, five) to give her two in order to make her a ten.

Five says, "okay," gives two to eight, and has only three left for himself. In the end, we have 10 and 3. We get 13.

$$8 + 5$$

$$10 + 3 = 13$$

We can also show the same thing this way →

$$8 + 5$$
$$8 + 2 + 3$$
$$10 + 3 = 13$$

1. Circle all of the blue marbles and enough of the yellow ones to make a ten. Add.

a.  $8 + 6$

$$10 + \_\_\_\_ = _____$$

b.  $8 + 7$

$$10 + \_\_\_\_ = _____$$

c.  $8 + 3$

$$10 + \_\_\_\_ = _____$$

d.  $8 + 4$

$$10 + \_\_\_\_ = _____$$

2. Fill in the blanks. Imagine that eight wants to become a ten.

a.
$$8 + 5$$
$$8 + \_\_\_ + \_\_\_\_$$
$$10 + \_\_\_\_ = _____$$

b.
$$8 + 8$$
$$8 + \_\_\_ + \_\_\_\_$$
$$10 + \_\_\_\_ = _____$$

3. How about if the second number is 8, such as $6 + 8$?
   Can you use the trick with 8 in that case?

4. Add.

   a. $8 + 6 =$ _____

   b. $6 + 9 =$ _____

   c. $9 + 4 =$ _____

   d. $4 + 8 =$ _____

   e. $8 + 7 =$ _____

   f. $9 + 9 =$ _____

   g. $9 + 5 =$ _____

   h. $8 + 8 =$ _____

   i. $3 + 8 =$ _____

5. Solve.

| a. Camilla found seven uniforms for the softball teams in one box, and six more uniforms in another box. How many uniforms did Camilla find? |
| --- |
| b. Three of the uniforms Camilla found were clean, but she had to wash the rest. How many uniforms did Camilla have to wash? |
| c. Eight girls and five boys came to play softball. How many more girls came than boys? |
| d. Did Camilla have enough uniforms for the boys and girls who came to play softball?<br><br>If not, how many more uniforms does she need?<br><br>If so, how many uniforms were left over? |

6. What number does the triangle represent?

| a. $\triangle + 8 = 16$ | b. $\triangle + 9 = 15$ | c. $\triangle + 2 + 7 = 13$ |
| --- | --- | --- |
| $\triangle =$ _____ | $\triangle =$ _____ | $\triangle =$ _____ |

# Add a Two-Digit and a Single-Digit Number

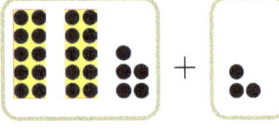 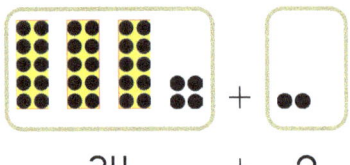

| 25 + 3 | 34 + 2 |
|---|---|
| Add the ones first: $5 + 3 = 8$. The 2 tens do not change. The sum is 28. | Add the ones first: $4 + 2 = 6$. The 3 tens do not change. The sum is 36. |

1. Write an addition equation for each illustration.

a.

_____ + _____ = _____

b.

_____ + _____ = _____

c.

_____ + _____ = _____

d.

_____ + _____ = _____

2. Add. Compare the problems. The top problem helps you solve the bottom one!

a.  $5 + 2 =$ _____

   $35 + 2 =$ _____

b.  $4 + 5 =$ _____

   $64 + 5 =$ _____

c.  $3 + 6 =$ _____

   $93 + 6 =$ _____

3. Add. Below each problem, write a "helping" problem with numbers less than 10.

a. $52 + 7 =$ _____

   $2 + 7 =$ _____

b. $33 + 1 =$ _____

   ___ + ___ = _____

c. $11 + 5 =$ _____

   ___ + ___ = _____

4. The numbers are written in boxes! Add the ones in their own column.
   Copy the number of tens to the answer box.

**Example:** 35 + 3

|  | tens | ones |
|---|---|---|
|  | 3 | 5 |
| + | ↓ | 3 |
|  | 3 | 8 |

12 + 6

**a.**

|  | tens | ones |
|---|---|---|
|  | 1 | 2 |
| + | ↓ | 6 |
|  |  |  |

57 + 1

**b.**

|  | tens | ones |
|---|---|---|
|  | 5 | 7 |
| + | ↓ | 1 |
|  |  |  |

64 + 3

**c.**

|  | tens | ones |
|---|---|---|
|  | 6 | 4 |
| + | ↓ | 3 |
|  |  |  |

5. Now *you* write the numbers in the boxes. Add the ones in their own column.

**a.** 26 + 3

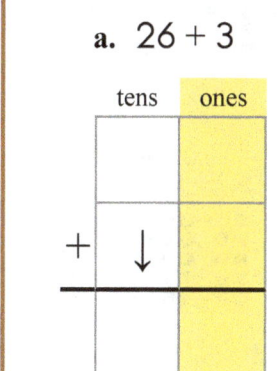

**b.** 72 + 4

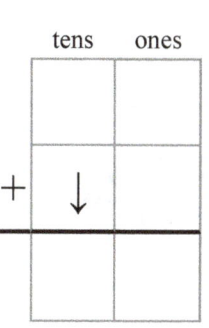

**c.** 65 + 4

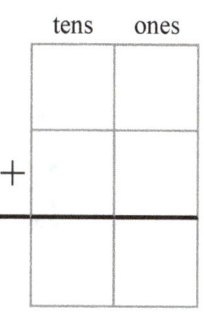

**d.** 81 + 7

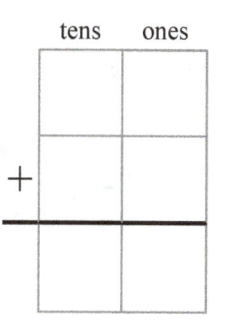

6. Add. Compare the problems.

| **a.** | **b.** | **c.** | **d.** |
|---|---|---|---|
| 6 + 2 = _____ | 4 + 3 = _____ | 5 + 4 = _____ | 1 + 7 = _____ |
| 16 + 2 = _____ | 24 + 3 = _____ | 45 + 4 = _____ | 61 + 7 = _____ |
| 36 + 2 = _____ | 34 + 3 = _____ | 65 + 4 = _____ | 41 + 7 = _____ |

Use the first problem to help you solve the one under it.

5 + 6 = _____          7 + 7 = _____          9 + 3 = _____

35 + 6 = _____          67 + 7 = _____          59 + 3 = _____

*Puzzle Corner*

# Subtract From the Ones

**14 – 2 = 12**

Subtract 4 – 2 = 2.
The ten stays the same.

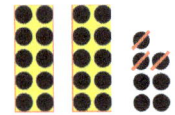

**27 – 3 = 24**

Subtract 7 – 3 = 4.
The two tens stay the same.

Subtract from the *ones*. Since we don't have to subtract from the tens, the tens do not change.

1. Subtract. You can cover dots to help you, or use the 100-bead abacus.

a. 28 – 2 = _____

b. 17 – 6 = _____

c. 37 – 7 = _____

d. 35 – 4 = _____

35 – 3 = _____

e. 57 – 7 = _____

57 – 3 = _____

f. 48 – 2 = _____

48 – 6 = _____

2. Subtract and compare. The top problem helps you solve the bottom one!

a. 6 – 4 = _____

56 – 4 = _____

b. 9 – 8 = _____

49 – 8 = _____

c. 5 – 2 = _____

95 – 2 = _____

3. Subtract. Think of the "helping problem" that uses only numbers less than 10.

a. 54 – 2 = _____

( 4 – 2 = ____ )

b. 76 – 3 = _____

( ____ – ____ = ____ )

c. 88 – 4 = _____

( ____ – ____ = ____ )

4. Draw a line from each problem to its answer.

$10 + \triangle = 15$            3            $65 + \triangle = 69$

                            4

$32 + \triangle = 38$                        $33 + \triangle = 36$

                            5

$72 + \triangle = 79$            6            $91 + \triangle = 98$

                            7

$54 + \triangle = 57$                        $44 + \triangle = 48$

5. Solve.

**a.** In the morning Katherine sold 11 pictures that she had painted, and in the afternoon she sold six. How many pictures did she sell in total?

**b.** She had 20 pictures to sell when she started. How many does she have left now?

6. Subtract.

**a.** $47 - 2 = $ _____        **b.** $57 - 4 = $ _____        **c.** $15 - 3 = $ _____

$75 - 1 = $ _____            $86 - 2 = $ _____            $98 - 4 = $ _____

7. Solve. In the last row, make your own problems, and let a friend solve them!

**a.** $\bigcirc + 2 = 88$                    **b.** $89 - \bigcirc = 85$

**c.** $\bigcirc - 5 = 20$                    **d.** $42 = 40 + \bigcirc$

$\bigcirc - $ _____ $ = $ _____            _____ $ + \bigcirc = $ _____

# More Practice

1. Subtract. You can cover dots to help you.

| | | |
|---|---|---|
| a. 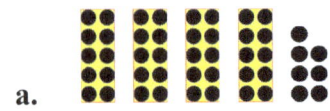 | b.  | c.  |
| $47 - 4 =$ _____ | $39 - 7 =$ _____ | $26 - 3 =$ _____ |
| $47 - 6 =$ _____ | $39 - 3 =$ _____ | $26 - 6 =$ _____ |

2. Add and subtract. Think of the "helping problem" that uses only numbers less than 10.

| | | |
|---|---|---|
| a. $45 + 2 =$ _____ <br> ( $5 + 2 =$ _____ ) | b. $63 + 5 =$ _____ <br> ( ___ + ___ = _____ ) | c. $92 + 5 =$ _____ <br> ( ___ + ___ = _____ ) |
| d. $67 - 2 =$ _____ <br> ( $7 - 2 =$ _____ ) | e. $54 - 3 =$ _____ <br> ( ___ − ___ = _____ ) | f. $99 - 7 =$ _____ <br> ( ___ − ___ = _____ ) |

3. Add and subtract. Compare the problems.

| a. | b. | c. |
|---|---|---|
| $55 + 4 =$ _____ | $64 - 3 =$ _____ | $46 - 4 =$ _____ |
| $25 + 4 =$ _____ | $34 - 3 =$ _____ | $96 - 4 =$ _____ |

4. Find what number the symbol stands for.

| | | |
|---|---|---|
| a. $37 - \bigcirc = 32$ <br><br> $\bigcirc =$ _____ | b. $52 + \bigcirc = 59$ <br><br> $\bigcirc =$ _____ | c. $67 - \bigcirc = 63$ <br><br> $\bigcirc =$ _____ |

5. Draw a line from each problem to its answer.

$11 + \triangle = 18$          4          $76 - \triangle = 72$

5

$83 + \triangle = 88$                     $99 - \triangle = 91$

6

$32 + \triangle = 39$          7          $56 - \triangle = 51$

8

$25 + \triangle = 29$                     $68 - \triangle = 62$

6. Write the numbers in the boxes. Add or subtract the ones in their own column.

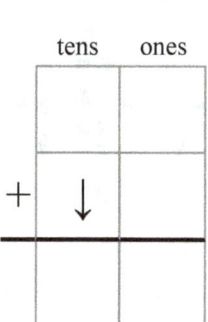

**a.** $35 + 3$

tens   ones

+   ↓

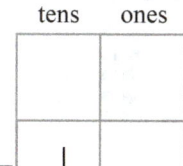

**b.** $56 - 4$

tens   ones

−   ↓

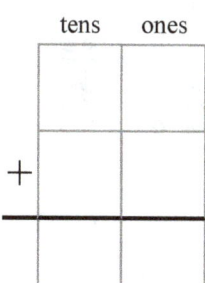

**c.** $41 + 8$

tens   ones

+

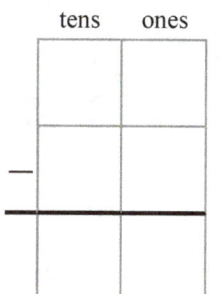

**d.** $78 - 7$

tens   ones

−

7. Solve.

**a.** Amy counted that there were 17 cups of yogurt in the fridge in the morning. In the evening there were only 11. How many had been eaten?

**b.** A recipe calls for six egg yolks. Mia is doubling the recipe. She has 9 eggs.

How many eggs does Mia need for the recipe?

How many more eggs does she need?

**Puzzle Corner**

Find the unknown number.

**a.** $33 + \triangle + \triangle = 39$          **b.** $99 - \triangle - \triangle = 91$

$\triangle = $ _____          $\triangle = $ _____

# Adding Two-Digit Numbers 1

When adding two-digit numbers, we add **ones to ones**, and **tens to tens**.

**Example 1.** We see there are a total of 5 tens, and a total of 8 ones.

The sum of 36 and 22 is 58.

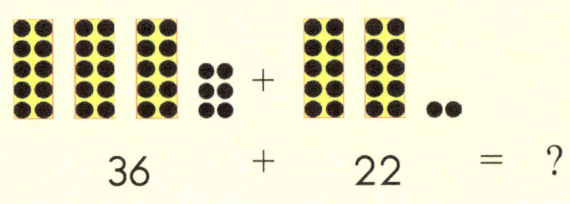

36    +    22    =    ?

1. Add. You can also use the 100-bead abacus to help you.

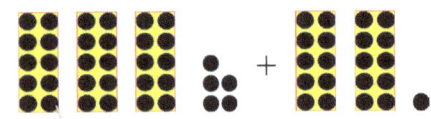

**a.** $35 + 21 =$ _____

**b.** $11 + 36 =$ _____

**c.** $25 + 24 =$ _____

2. Write the addition equation that the pictures illustrate.

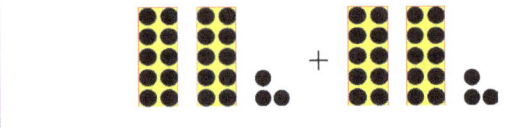

**a.** _____ + _____ = _____

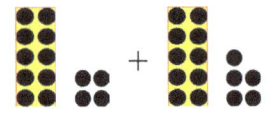

**b.** _____ + _____ = _____

**c.** _____ + _____ = _____

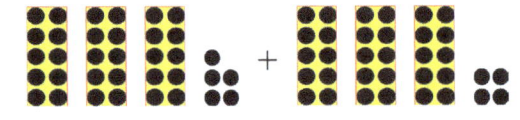

**d.** _____ + _____ = _____

3. You can do these problems in your head.

| | | |
|---|---|---|
| **a.** $30 + 20 =$ _____ | **b.** $40 + 60 =$ _____ | **c.** $60 - 40 =$ _____ |
| $60 + 20 =$ _____ | $30 + 30 =$ _____ | $70 - 50 =$ _____ |

**Example 2.** On the right, we add 74 and 13.

We add the tens and the ones separately.

74 + 13 equals 87.

$$
\begin{array}{rl}
& 7 \text{ tens} \quad 4 \text{ ones} \\
+ & 1 \text{ ten} \quad\ \ 3 \text{ ones} \\
\hline
& 8 \text{ tens} \quad 7 \text{ ones} \ = 87
\end{array}
$$

4. Add.

**a.** 52 + 36 = ?

$$
\begin{array}{rl}
& 5 \text{ tens} \quad 2 \text{ ones} \\
+ & 3 \text{ tens} \quad 6 \text{ ones} \\
\hline
& \phantom{0}\text{ tens} \quad \phantom{0}\text{ ones} \ = \underline{\phantom{xxx}}
\end{array}
$$

**b.** 15 + 44 = ?

$$
\begin{array}{rl}
& 1 \text{ ten} \quad\ 5 \text{ ones} \\
+ & 4 \text{ tens} \quad 4 \text{ ones} \\
\hline
& \phantom{0}\text{ tens} \quad \phantom{0}\text{ ones} \ = \underline{\phantom{xxx}}
\end{array}
$$

**c.** 27 + 41 = ?

$$
\begin{array}{rl}
& \phantom{0}\text{ tens} \quad \phantom{0}\text{ ones} \\
+ & \phantom{0}\text{ tens} \quad \phantom{0}\text{ one} \\
\hline
& \phantom{0}\text{ tens} \quad \phantom{0}\text{ ones} \ = \underline{\phantom{xxx}}
\end{array}
$$

**d.** 74 + 23 = ?

$$
\begin{array}{rl}
& \phantom{0}\text{ tens} \quad \phantom{0}\text{ ones} \\
+ & \phantom{0}\text{ tens} \quad \phantom{0}\text{ ones} \\
\hline
& \phantom{0}\text{ tens} \quad \phantom{0}\text{ ones} \ = \underline{\phantom{xxx}}
\end{array}
$$

**e.** 16 + 53 = ?

$$
\begin{array}{rl}
& \phantom{0}\text{ ten} \quad \phantom{0}\text{ ones} \\
+ & \phantom{0}\text{ tens} \quad \phantom{0}\text{ ones} \\
\hline
& \phantom{0}\text{ tens} \quad \phantom{0}\text{ ones} \ = \underline{\phantom{xxx}}
\end{array}
$$

**f.** 63 + 24 = ?

$$
\begin{array}{rl}
& \phantom{0}\text{ tens} \quad \phantom{0}\text{ ones} \\
+ & \phantom{0}\text{ tens} \quad \phantom{0}\text{ ones} \\
\hline
& \phantom{0}\text{ tens} \quad \phantom{0}\text{ ones} \ = \underline{\phantom{xxx}}
\end{array}
$$

**g.** 12 + 23 + 44 = ?

$$
\begin{array}{rl}
& \phantom{0}\text{ ten} \quad \phantom{0}\text{ ones} \\
& \phantom{0}\text{ tens} \quad \phantom{0}\text{ ones} \\
+ & \phantom{0}\text{ tens} \quad \phantom{0}\text{ ones} \\
\hline
& \phantom{0}\text{ tens} \quad \phantom{0}\text{ ones} \ = \underline{\phantom{xxx}}
\end{array}
$$

**h.** 35 + 30 + 22 = ?

$$
\begin{array}{rl}
& \phantom{0}\text{ tens} \quad \phantom{0}\text{ ones} \\
& \phantom{0}\text{ tens} \quad \phantom{0}\text{ ones} \\
+ & \phantom{0}\text{ tens} \quad \phantom{0}\text{ ones} \\
\hline
& \phantom{0}\text{ tens} \quad \phantom{0}\text{ ones} \ = \underline{\phantom{xxx}}
\end{array}
$$

5. (Challenge) Add.     **a.** 73 + 25         **b.** 35 + 25         **c.** 14 + 16

We can also write the numbers to be added in a grid. Then we add **the ones** in their own column, and **the tens** in their own column.

**Example 1.**

| | tens | ones |
|---|---|---|
| | 4 | 5 |
| + | 2 | 3 |
| | 6 | 8 |

This addition is 45 + 23 = 68.

**Example 2.**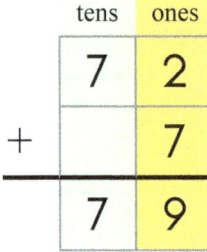

Here, the second number has *no* tens. What numbers were added?

6. Add. If the number has no tens, you may write a zero in the tens place for clarity.

**a.**

| | tens | ones |
|---|---|---|
| | 5 | 3 |
| + | 2 | 6 |
| | | |

**b.**

| | tens | ones |
|---|---|---|
| | 1 | 3 |
| + | 8 | 4 |
| | | |

**c.**

| | tens | ones |
|---|---|---|
| | 3 | 5 |
| + | 0 | 4 |
| | | |

**d.**

| | | |
|---|---|---|
| | 6 | 2 |
| + | | 6 |
| | | |

**e.**

| | | |
|---|---|---|
| | 2 | 5 |
| + | 5 | 3 |
| | | |

**f.**

| | | |
|---|---|---|
| | 9 | 2 |
| + | | 7 |
| | | |

7. Write one number under the other in the grid, and add.

**a.** 17 + 21

**b.** 42 + 56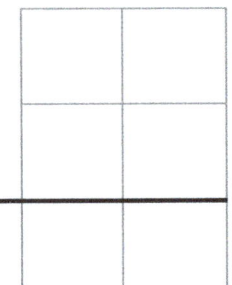

**c.** 34 + 14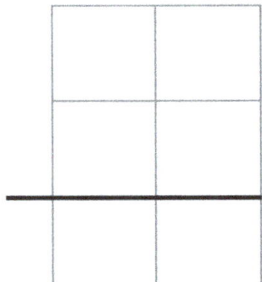

**d.** 51 + 6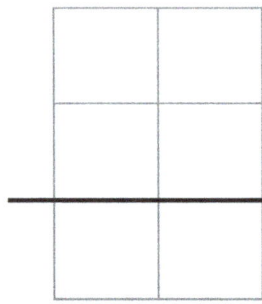

# Completing the Next Ten

| Review:<br>What numbers make 10?<br><br>You need to remember<br>these well! | 1 + _____ = 10 | 8 + _____ = 10 | 3 + _____ = 10 |
| --- | --- | --- | --- |
| | 7 + _____ = 10 | 5 + _____ = 10 | 6 + _____ = 10 |
| | 4 + _____ = 10 | 9 + _____ = 10 | 2 + _____ = 10 |

### Completing the ten

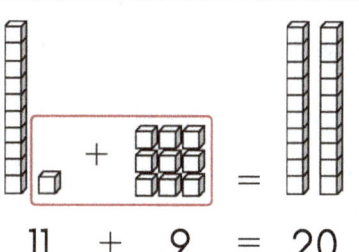

11 + 9 = 20

The 1 and the 9 single blocks make a *new* ten. We get a total of 20.

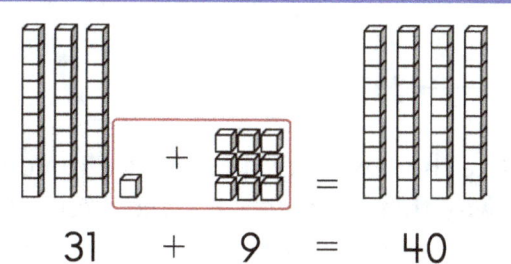

31 + 9 = 40

The 1 and the 9 single blocks make a *new* ten. We get a total of 40.

1. Draw more single blocks until there are ten of them. Circle the new ten.
   Write the addition that completes the next ten. You can also do these with an abacus.

a.

33 + ____ = _40_

b.

43 + ____ = _____

c.

27 + ____ = _____

d.

36 + ____ = _____

e.

62 + ____ = _____

f.

54 + ____ = _____

2. Complete the next ten. Think of the "helping problem" where you complete 10.

**a.** $23 +$ _____ $= 30$

($3 +$ _____ $= 10$)

**b.** $44 +$ _____ $=$ _____

( _____ $+$ _____ $= 10$)

**c.** $17 +$ _____ $=$ _____

( _____ $+$ _____ $= 10$)

3. Complete the next ten. Think of the helping problem where you complete 10.

**a.** $13 +$ _____ $= 20$

**b.** $44 +$ _____ $=$ _____

**c.** $88 +$ _____ $=$ _____

**d.** $96 +$ _____ $=$ _____

**e.** $79 +$ _____ $=$ _____

**f.** $37 +$ _____ $=$ _____

**g.** $91 +$ _____ $=$ _____

**h.** $65 +$ _____ $=$ _____

4. Complete the next ten. Then write a matching subtraction using the same numbers, in such a way that the number in the oval is the same in both problems.

**a.** $36 + \bigcirc = 40$

$40 - \bigcirc = 36$

**b.** $57 + \bigcirc =$ _____

_____ $- \bigcirc =$ _____

**c.** $64 + \bigcirc =$ _____

_____ $- \bigcirc =$ _____

**d.** $95 + \bigcirc =$ _____

_____ $- \bigcirc =$ _____

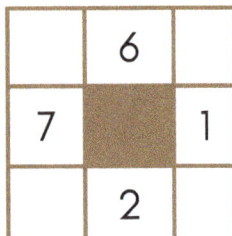

**Puzzle Corner** Place numbers in the boxes so that the sum of each row and each column is 15. (Do not use the middle square.)

| | 6 | |
|---|---|---|
| 7 | | 1 |
| | 2 | |

| | 7 | |
|---|---|---|
| 5 | | 8 |
| | 6 | |

| | 4 | |
|---|---|---|
| 3 | | 3 |
| | 2 | |

# Going Over the Next Ten

> **Remember?**
>
> 10 plus 3, 4, 5, 6, 7, 8, or 9
> makes one of the **TEEN** numbers!
>
> 10 plus <u>three</u> is <u>thir</u>teen.
> 10 plus <u>six</u> is <u>six</u>teen.
> 10 plus <u>nine</u> is <u>nine</u>teen.
> 10 plus <u>five</u> is <u>fif</u>teen.

1. Add.   **a.** $10 + 4 = $ _____     **b.** $10 + 7 = $ _____     **c.** $10 + 8 = $ _____

| | |
|---|---|
| $6 \;+\; 8$ <br> $\rightarrow 10 \;+\; 4$ <br><br> We circle TEN marbles to make a ten. We can now see that there are 10 and 4 marbles. $10 + 4 = 14$. So $6 + 8 = 14$. | $7 \;+\; 5$ <br> $\rightarrow 10 \;+\; 2$ <br><br> We circle TEN marbles to make a ten. We can now see that there are 10 and 2 marbles. $10 + 2 = 12$. So $7 + 5 = 12$. |

2. First circle ten marbles to make a ten. How many marbles are there in all?

| | |
|---|---|
| **a.** <br> $7 \;+\; 8$ <br> $\rightarrow \quad 10 \;+\;$ ____ $=$ _____ | **b.** <br> $8 \;+\; 9$ <br> $\rightarrow \quad 10 \;+\;$ ____ $=$ _____ |
| **c.** <br> $6 \;+\; 5$ <br> $\rightarrow \quad 10 \;+\;$ ____ $=$ _____ | **d.** <br> $9 \;+\; 4$ <br> $\rightarrow \quad 10 \;+\;$ ____ $=$ _____ |
| **e.** <br> $8 \;+\; 5$ <br> $\rightarrow \quad 10 \;+\;$ ____ $=$ _____ | **f.** <br> $7 \;+\; 7$ <br> $\rightarrow \quad 10 \;+\;$ ____ $=$ _____ |

## Sums that go over to the next ten

Let's add 59 + 5. *First* we complete 60.

59 + 5

59 + 1 + 4

60 + 4 = 64

Because 59 + 1 = 60, we split the 5 into 1 and 4. The 1 goes with the 59 to make 60. Then the 60 and the 4 left over make 64.

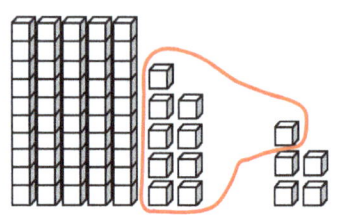

9 and 1 make a new ten. We get 6 tens.

59 + 5 = 64

3. Circle ten single cubes to make a ten. Count the tens and ones. Write the answer.

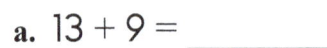

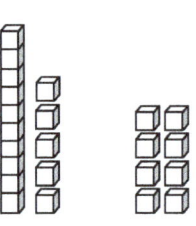

**a.** 13 + 9 = _____

**b.** 15 + 8 = _____

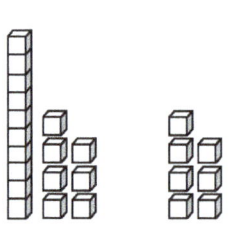

**c.** 17 + 7 = _____

**d.** 24 + 7 = _____

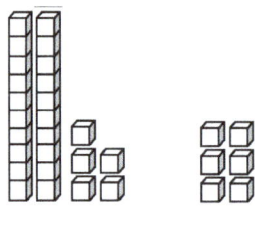

**e.** 25 + 6 = _____

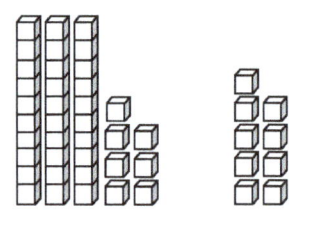

**f.** 37 + 9 = _____

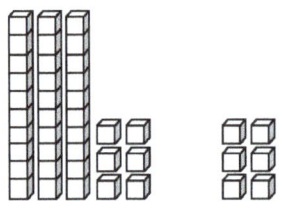

**g.** 36 + 6 = _____

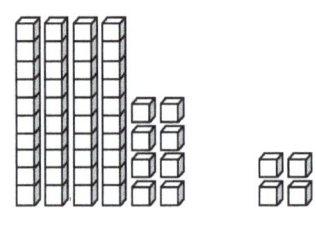

**h.** 48 + 4 = _____

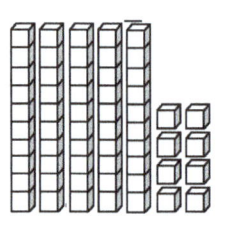

**i.** 58 + 5 = _____

4. Add. First make a new ten with some of the single dots. You can also use the abacus.

a. 25 + 15 = _____

b. 37 + 24 = _____

c. 17 + 18 = _____

d. 14 + 48 = _____

5. Write the addition equation. You can circle the new ten you get from the ones.

a. _____ + _____ = _____

b. _____ + _____ = _____

c. _____ + _____ = _____

d. _____ + _____ = _____

6. Add. Sometimes you can make a new ten and sometimes not.

a.

36 + 16 = _____

b.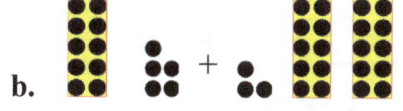

15 + 23 = _____

c.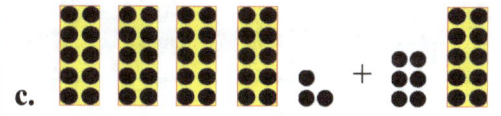

43 + 16 = _____

d. 25 + 37 = _____

# Adding Within 20, Part 1

In recent lessons, you have learned several ways to add. Let's review them:

| | |
|---|---|
| 1. The trick with nine and eight.<br><br>$9 + 6 = ?$<br><br>Think of nine wanting to be ten, so six gives one to nine. Then the addition becomes $10 + 5$, which is 15. | 2. Just one more than an addition you know.<br><br>For example, $3 + 7 = 10$, so $3 + 8$ must be just one more, or 11. |
| 3. The doubles:<br><br>    $5 + 5 =$ _____<br><br>    $6 + 6 =$ _____<br><br>    $7 + 7 =$ _____<br><br>    $8 + 8 =$ _____<br><br>    $9 + 9 =$ _____ | 4. Just one more than a double:<br><br>$7 + 8$ is just one more than $7 + 7$.<br><br>Since $7 + 7$ is 14, then $7 + 8$ must be 15. |

1. Draw a line between each doubles fact and the addition that is "just one more". Solve.

$5 + 6 =$ _____     $4 + 4 =$ _____     $7 + 7 =$ _____     $8 + 9 =$ _____

$9 + 9 =$ _____     $9 + 10 =$ _____     $6 + 7 =$ _____     $8 + 7 =$ _____

$5 + 4 =$ _____     $5 + 5 =$ _____     $8 + 8 =$ _____     $6 + 6 =$ _____

2. Find the addition equations that are wrong, and correct them.
   (Note: there are several different ways to make the corrections.)

| | | |
|---|---|---|
| **a.** $9 + 8 = 17$ | **b.** $3 + 9 = 11$ | **c.** $14 = 8 + 6$ |
| **d.** $16 = 9 + 6$ | **e.** $15 = 8 + 8$ | **f.** $5 + 8 = 13$ |

3. For each sum of 10 write another that is "just one more."

| a. $1 + 9 = 10$ | b. $3 + 7 = 10$ | c. $8 + 2 = 10$ |
|---|---|---|
| _____ + _____ = 11 | _____ + _____ = 11 | _____ + _____ = 11 |
| d. $6 + 4 = 10$ | e. $5 + 5 = 10$ | f. $7 + 3 = 10$ |
| _____ + _____ = 11 | _____ + _____ = 11 | _____ + _____ = 11 |

4. Solve.

a. Ashley had 9 shirts and her brother Andy had 8.
Then they both got three new shirts from their aunt.

How many shirts does Ashley have now?

And Andy?

Who has more shirts now?

How many more?

b. Mia counted the chairs in their house. She counted four in the office, four in all the bedrooms, and five in the kitchen. How many chairs is that in total?

5. Add. Tell which idea you use to add.

Trick with nine

Trick with eight

"Just one more" than a sum with 10

a. $7 + 7 = $ _____    b. $9 + 7 = $ _____    Doubles facts

c. $8 + 3 = $ _____    d. $6 + 7 = $ _____    Just one more than a double

e. $5 + 6 = $ _____    f. $5 + 8 = $ _____    I just know it!

g. $8 + 8 = $ _____    h. $4 + 9 = $ _____

6. Add.

| a. $8 + 2 + 3 =$ | b. $9 + 5 + 2 =$ | c. $12 + 2 + 2 =$ |
|---|---|---|
| d. $5 + 6 + 6 =$ | e. $4 + 4 + 4 =$ | f. $13 + 5 + 1 =$ |
| g. $7 + 7 + 3 =$ | h. $6 + 8 + 6 =$ | i. $14 + 3 + 3 =$ |

7. Solve.

a. Joe has five pencils in his pencil case, four in a can, and five more scattered on the table. How many pencils does Joe have?

b. María has nine paper airplanes. Her brother Juan has five more than María. How many does Juan have?

c. María made three new paper airplanes for herself. How many does she have now?

d. Bill counted all the fruit in the house. He found 11 bananas in the kitchen, and five apples and three kiwis in the fridge. How many pieces of fruit did Bill find?

**Puzzle Corner**

Compare, and write $<$ , $>$, or $=$ in the box.
Note: Often you can compare without calculating anything!

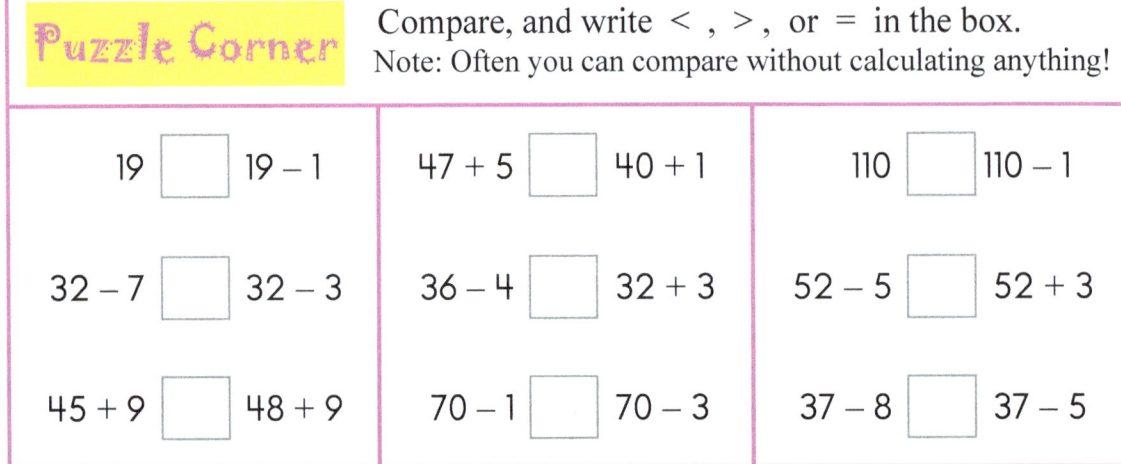

| $19$ ☐ $19 - 1$ | $47 + 5$ ☐ $40 + 1$ | $110$ ☐ $110 - 1$ |
|---|---|---|
| $32 - 7$ ☐ $32 - 3$ | $36 - 4$ ☐ $32 + 3$ | $52 - 5$ ☐ $52 + 3$ |
| $45 + 9$ ☐ $48 + 9$ | $70 - 1$ ☐ $70 - 3$ | $37 - 8$ ☐ $37 - 5$ |

# Adding Within 20, Part 2

1. Add. (Remember, if you find two numbers that make 10, add those first.)

| a. | b. | c. |
|---|---|---|
| $8 + 8 + 2 =$ _____ | $1 + 6 + 6 =$ _____ | $4 + 4 + 4 =$ _____ |
| $7 + 7 + 1 =$ _____ | $3 + 2 + 7 =$ _____ | $5 + 5 + 5 =$ _____ |

| d. | e. | f. |
|---|---|---|
| $5 + 6 + 4 =$ _____ | $2 + 8 + 7 =$ _____ | $6 + 6 + 6 =$ _____ |
| $3 + 5 + 6 =$ _____ | $3 + 7 + 7 =$ _____ | $7 + 7 + 4 =$ _____ |

2. Solve.

a. Caden put 4 toy cars in a line, 7 cars in another, and 6 cars in a third line.
   How many cars in total did he use?

b. Natalie and Eric went to play tennis. They had 16 tennis balls with them.
   During the game they lost two balls.
   How many tennis balls do they have now?



   Later they found four balls near the tennis court that other people had lost.
   Now how many tennis balls do they have?

c. Aria had some playing cards in her hand. She gave seven cards to her sister and six
   to her brother. That left four cards for her. How many cards did she have initially?

3. Find the pattern in these problems and their answers! Solve.

| a. | b. | c. | d. |
|---|---|---|---|
| 8 + 2 = _____ | 5 + 3 = _____ | 9 + 2 = _____ | 7 + 3 = _____ |
| 8 + 4 = _____ | 5 + 5 = _____ | 9 + 4 = _____ | 7 + 5 = _____ |
| 8 + 6 = _____ | 5 + 7 = _____ | 9 + 6 = _____ | 7 + 7 = _____ |
| 8 + 8 = _____ | 5 + 9 = _____ | 9 + 8 = _____ | 7 + 9 = _____ |

4. Make two *different* addition problems with the given sums (answers).

a. _____ + _____ + _____ = 12        b. _____ + _____ + _____ = 14

_____ + _____ + _____ = 12        _____ + _____ + _____ = 14

5. Correct or not? Cross out the equations that are false.

a. $5 + 7 = 12$        b. $16 = 8 + 9$        c. $6 + 6 = 5 + 8$

d. $11 + 4 = 14$        e. $7 + 8 = 14$        f. $3 + 8 = 9 + 2$

**Puzzle Corner**    Find two different solutions to the puzzle.

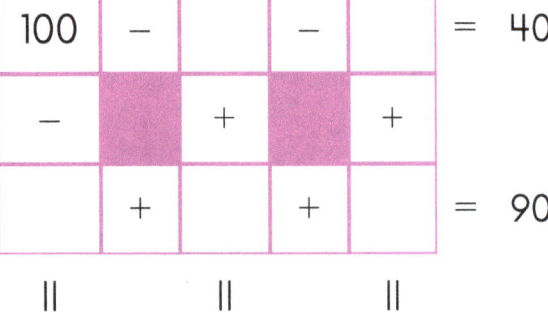
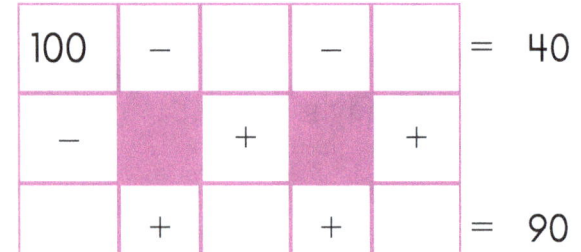

126

# Adding Two-Digit Numbers 2

Here, we get **a new ten** from the ones.
What is the total?

18 + 33 = _____

Here is the same addition written differently.
Adding 18 + 33 gives us 4 tens and 11 ones.
The 11 ones make a new ten.

So, the final answer is 5 tens and 1 one,
or _____ .

|  | 1 ten | 8 ones |
|---|---|---|
| + | 3 tens | 3 ones |
|  | 4 tens | 11 ones = _____ |

1. Add.

**a.**
```
   3 tens    5 ones
 + 3 tens    6 ones
 _____
   ____ tens  ____ ones = _____
```

**b.**
```
   5 tens    8 ones
 + 2 tens    4 ones
 _____
      tens       ones = _____
```

**c.**
```
   2 tens    4 ones
 + 6 tens    7 ones
 _____
      tens       ones = _____
```

**d.**
```
   4 tens    9 ones
 + 3 tens    3 ones
 _____
      tens       ones = _____
```

**e.**
```
   3 tens    5 ones
 + 3 tens    3 ones
 _____
      tens       ones = _____
```

**f.**
```
   2 tens    6 ones
 + 5 tens    4 ones
 _____
                    = _____
```

**g.**
```
   2 tens    1 ones
 + 7 tens    8 ones
 _____
                    = _____
```

**h.**
```
   1 ten     6 ones
 + 5 tens    5 ones
 _____
                    = _____
```

2. Complete. Split the second number into two parts so that you can complete the next
ten. You can also use your abacus to solve these.

| a.  28 + 8 $\phantom{}$ / \ <br><br> 28 + _2_ + _6_ <br><br> 30 + ___ = _____ | b.  47 + 5 $\phantom{}$ / \ <br><br> 47 + _3_ + ___ <br><br> 50 + ___ = _____ | c.  79 + 9 $\phantom{}$ / \ <br><br> 79 + ___ + ___ <br><br> 80 + ___ = _____ |
|---|---|---|
| d.  39 + 3 $\phantom{}$ / \ <br><br> 39 + ___ + ___ <br><br> 40 + __ = _____ | e.  27 + 5 $\phantom{}$ / \ <br><br> 27 + ___ + ___ <br><br> _____ + __ = _____ | f.  38 + 7 $\phantom{}$ / \ <br><br> 38 + ___ + ___ <br><br> _____ + __ = _____ |

3. Solve the problems. You can use an abacus, write the numbers in a grid, or split
the numbers like in the previous exercises.

a. Mom and Amy made crackers. One pan had 42 crackers,
another had 30, and the last one had 5.
How many crackers did they make in total?

b. Jessica had 34 colored pencils and Matt had 22.
How many do they have together?

c. Jessica gave Matt 6 pencils. Now how many does Matt have?

d. Caleb took 11 strawberries and ate them. Then he
decided to eat five more. Later, he ate 4 more.
How many strawberries did he eat in total?

# Addition Practice

1. What number goes in the rectangle?

| | |
|---|---|
| **a.** $6 + 6 + \boxed{\phantom{00}} = 15$ | **b.** $5 + \boxed{\phantom{00}} + 5 = 16$ |
| **c.** $2 + 4 + \boxed{\phantom{00}} = 12$ | **d.** $7 + 4 + \boxed{\phantom{00}} = 11$ |
| **e.** $\boxed{\phantom{00}} + 8 + 1 = 13$ | **f.** $6 + \boxed{\phantom{00}} + 2 = 15$ |

2. Solve.

> **a.** Jackson counted his shirts. He had seven T-shirts in one drawer and three long-sleeve shirts in another. Then he remembered that two shirts were in the wash. How many shirts does Jackson have?

> **b.** There are two fruit bowls on the table. One has six bananas. The other has apples. There are two fewer bananas than apples. How many apples are in the bowl?

> **c.** Muhammad was putting away cookies. He put 8 cookies in one container and 8 in another. There were still three cookies on the pan. How many cookies in total were there?

3. Add and subtract. Start at the bottom left corner and follow the arrows.

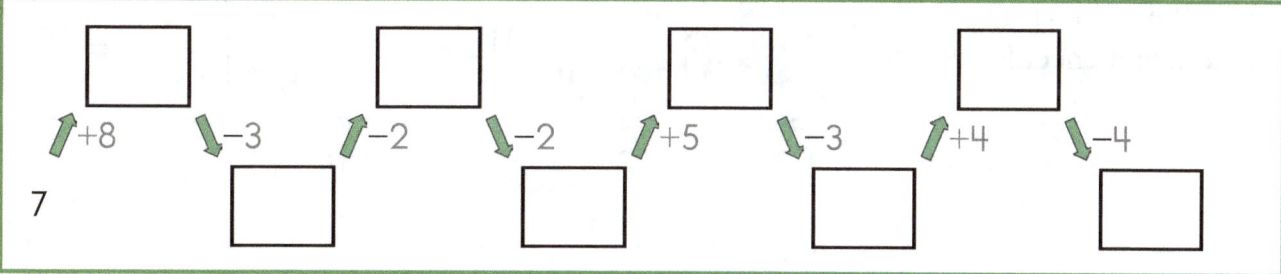

4. *A challenge!* Here are ALL the basic addition facts where the sum is more than 10.
   How many of them can you solve? We will study these more in second grade.

| a. | b. | c. | d. |
|---|---|---|---|
| 8 + 8 = _____ | 7 + 8 = _____ | 7 + 7 = _____ | 5 + 8 = _____ |
| 2 + 9 = _____ | 9 + 6 = _____ | 9 + 8 = _____ | 3 + 9 = _____ |
| 7 + 5 = _____ | 6 + 5 = _____ | 7 + 4 = _____ | 7 + 6 = _____ |
| e. | f. | g. | h. |
| 9 + 4 = _____ | 8 + 6 = _____ | 9 + 2 = _____ | 6 + 9 = _____ |
| 4 + 8 = _____ | 6 + 6 = _____ | 8 + 5 = _____ | 8 + 7 = _____ |
| 6 + 7 = _____ | 5 + 9 = _____ | 5 + 7 = _____ | 8 + 4 = _____ |
| i. | j. | k. | l. |
| 9 + 3 = _____ | 4 + 9 = _____ | 9 + 9 = _____ | 8 + 9 = _____ |
| 4 + 7 = _____ | 7 + 7 = _____ | 6 + 8 = _____ | 5 + 6 = _____ |
| 9 + 5 = _____ | 3 + 8 = _____ | 6 + 6 = _____ | 8 + 3 = _____ |

**Puzzle Corner**

What numbers can go into these puzzles? Guess and check!

(Try to find several solutions! You can copy the puzzles to blank paper.)

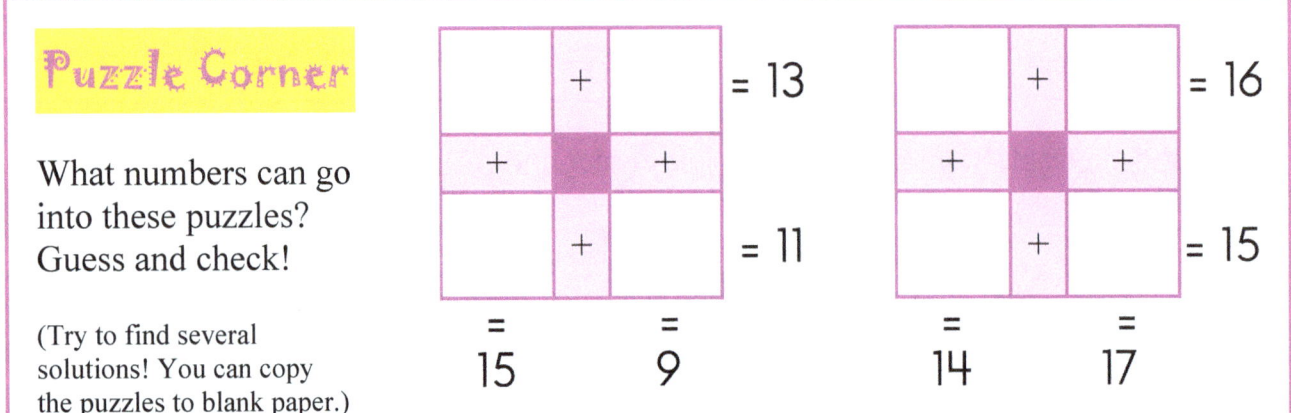

130

# Subtract to 10

1. Subtract the dots that are not in the ten-group. You should only have ten left!

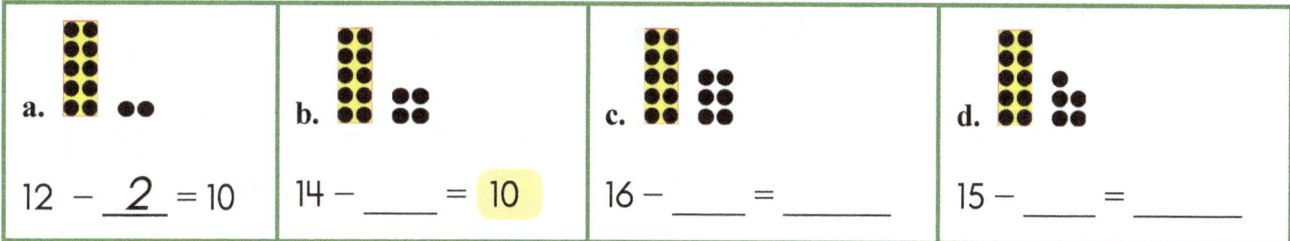

a. $12 - \underline{\ 2\ } = 10$

b. $14 - \underline{\quad} = 10$

c. $16 - \underline{\quad} = \underline{\quad\quad}$

d. $15 - \underline{\quad} = \underline{\quad\quad}$

2. Subtract the "ones" so that 10 is left.

a. $13 - \underline{\quad} = 10$

b. $17 - \underline{\quad} = \underline{\quad\quad}$

c. $19 - \underline{\quad} = \underline{\quad\quad}$

---

**Subtracting in parts**

Let's subtract 13 − 5 in two parts. First we subtract enough dots so that we have only 10 left. So we take away 3 dots: $13 - 3 = 10$.
(Cross out the three individual dots from the picture.)

We still need to subtract 2 more. We subtract those from the 10. There are 8 left.
(Cross out two dots from the ten.)

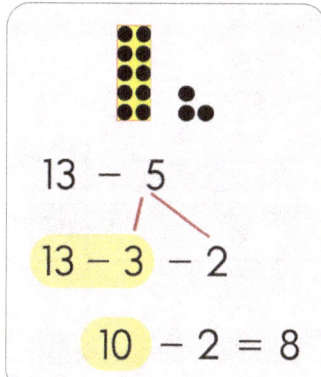

$13 - 5$

$13 - 3 \ - 2$

$10 \ - 2 = 8$

---

3. First subtract enough dots so that you have only 10 left. Then subtract the rest.

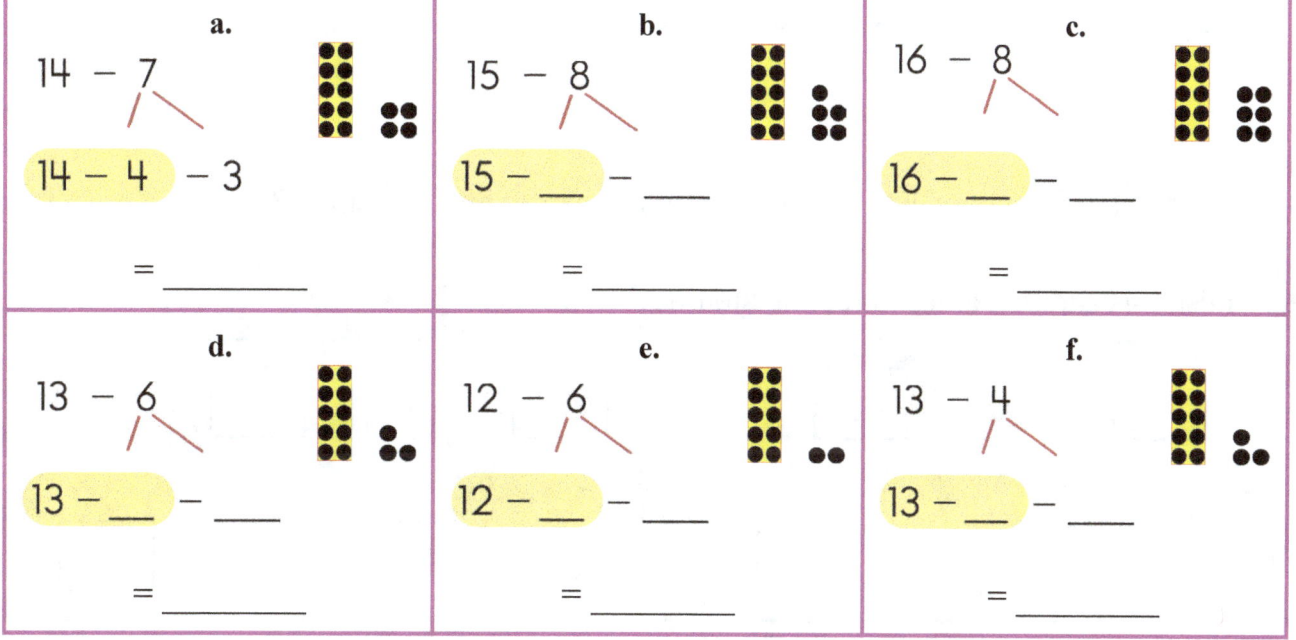

a. $14 - 7$

$14 - 4 \ - 3$

$= \underline{\quad\quad}$

b. $15 - 8$

$15 - \underline{\ } \ - \underline{\ }$

$= \underline{\quad\quad}$

c. $16 - 8$

$16 - \underline{\ } \ - \underline{\ }$

$= \underline{\quad\quad}$

d. $13 - 6$

$13 - \underline{\ } \ - \underline{\ }$

$= \underline{\quad\quad}$

e. $12 - 6$

$12 - \underline{\ } \ - \underline{\ }$

$= \underline{\quad\quad}$

f. $13 - 4$

$13 - \underline{\ } \ - \underline{\ }$

$= \underline{\quad\quad}$

4. First subtract to 10. Then subtract the rest.

| **a.** 12 − 6 <br><br> 12 − _2_ − 4 <br><br> = ____ | **b.** 15 − 9 <br><br> 15 − ____ − ____ <br><br> = ____ | **c.** 13 − 8 <br><br> 13 − ____ − ____ <br><br> = ____ |
|---|---|---|
| **d.** 13 − 7 <br><br> 13 − ____ − ____ <br><br> = ____ | **e.** 14 − 7 <br><br> 14 − ____ − ____ <br><br> = ____ | **f.** 12 − 4 <br><br> 12 − ____ − ____ <br><br> = ____ |

5. Subtract. You can use the dots to help you.

| **a.** <br> 12 − 5 = ____ | **b.** <br> 14 − 6 = ____ | **c.** <br> 13 − 6 = ____ | **d.** <br> 15 − 7 = ____ |
|---|---|---|---|
| **e.** <br> 15 − 6 = ____ | **f.** <br> 14 − 5 = ____ | **g.** <br> 16 − 8 = ____ | **h.** <br> 13 − 4 = ____ |

6. Tom is 13, Juan is 8, and Alice is 9.

   **a.** How many years older is Tom than Juan?

   **b.** How many years older is Tom than Alice?

   **c.** Two years from now, how many years older than Juan will Tom be?

7. Finish this addition and subtraction "journey"!

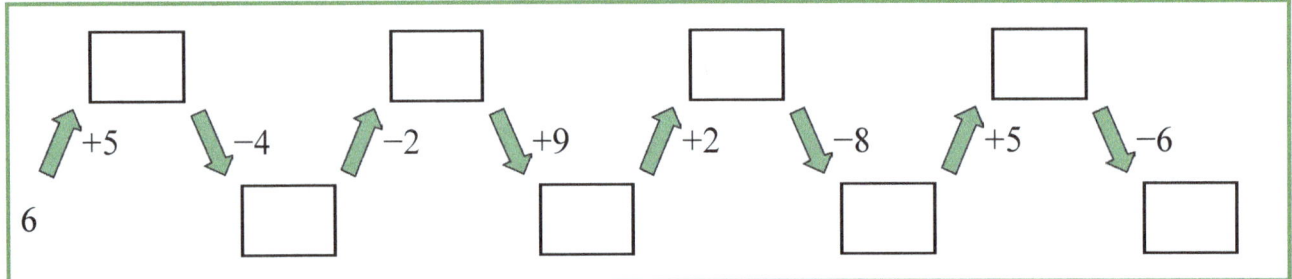

# Using Addition to Subtract 1

From the picture on the right we can write two additions and two subtractions: a **fact family**.

There are TWO parts that make up the total, 6 and 5. In addition, we add the parts and get the total.

In subtraction, we start with the total and take away one of the parts. What is left? The other part.

**Fact family with 6, 5, and 11:**

$6 + 5 = 11$ $\qquad$ $11 - 5 = 6$

$5 + 6 = 11$ $\qquad$ $11 - 6 = 5$

1. Write fact families.

**a.**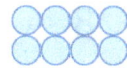

_____ + _____ = _____

_____ + _____ = _____

_____ − _____ = _____

_____ − _____ = _____

**b.**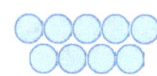

_____ + _____ = _____

_____ + _____ = _____

_____ − _____ = _____

_____ − _____ = _____

2. Calculate the total. Write two matching subtractions using the same numbers.

**a.** $8 + 4 =$ _____

_____ − _____ = _____

_____ − _____ = _____

**b.** $9 + 7 =$ _____

_____ − _____ = _____

_____ − _____ = _____

**c.** $7 + 6 =$ _____

_____ − _____ = _____

_____ − _____ = _____

3. For each subtraction write the matching addition.

**a.** $11 - 3 =$ _____

$3 +$ _____ $= 11$

**b.** $11 - 4 =$ _____

_____ $+$ _____ $= 11$

**c.** $12 - 3 =$ _____

_____ $+$ _____ $= 12$

You can solve a subtraction problem like $15 - 9$ or $16 - 8$ **by addition**.

| $15 - 9 = ?$ | $16 - 8 = ?$ |
|---|---|
| Think: $9 +$ _____ $= 15$ | Think: $8 +$ _____ $= 16$ |
| Or 9 and how many more is 15? | Or 8 and what number makes 16? |
| Guess and check! | Guess and check! |
| Will $9 + 8$ work? Or $9 + 7$? Or $9 + 6$? Or $9 + 5$? You can use the trick with nine! | Will $8 + 5$ work? Or $8 + 6$? Or $8 + 7$? |

4. Solve each subtraction by thinking about the matching addition.

| a. $14 - 8 =$ _____ $(8 +$ _____ $= 14)$ | b. $15 - 7 =$ _____ $(7 +$ _____ $= 15)$ | c. $17 - 8 =$ _____ $(8 +$ _____ $= 17)$ |
|---|---|---|
| d. $12 - 8 =$ _____ $($ _____ $+$ _____ $= 12)$ | e. $16 - 7 =$ _____ $($ _____ $+$ _____ $= 16)$ | f. $13 - 7 =$ _____ $($ _____ $+$ _____ $= 13)$ |
| g. $13 - 8 =$ _____ | h. $11 - 7 =$ _____ | i. $14 - 9 =$ _____ |

5. Doubles and doubles plus one more! Solve. Also, match each addition to the subtraction in the same fact family.

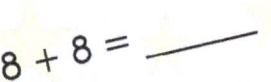
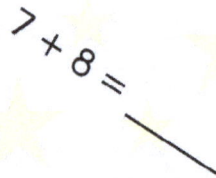

$8 + 8 =$ _____

$7 + 8 =$ _____

$17 - 8 =$ _____

$15 - 7 =$ _____

$16 - 8 =$ _____

$7 + 7 =$ _____

$14 - 7 =$ _____

$8 + 9 =$ _____

# Using Addition to Subtract 2

1. Solve by thinking of addition.

| a. $12 - 8 =$ _____ | b. $11 - 7 =$ _____ | c. $13 - 9 =$ _____ |
|---|---|---|
| d. $15 - 6 =$ _____ | e. $18 - 9 =$ _____ | f. $16 - 7 =$ _____ |

2. Which equation(s) match the problem?

Ava had 9 darts in her hand. She threw three of them missing the target. Then she threw three more and hit the target on each one! How many darts does she now have in her hand?

$9 - 3 - 3 =$ _____

$9 + 3 + 3 =$ _____

$3 + 3 +$ _____ $= 9$

3. Solve.

a. Marsha took 11 crayons from the crayon box, Susana took 6. and Lena took 2. Now the crayon box is empty! Now how many crayons were in the box at first?

b. How many more crayons does Marsha have than Lena?

c. Luna counted 14 stars in her drawing, and she thought, "That is too many." So she erased five of them. How many stars are in her drawing now?

d. Elijah counted his toy cars and said, "I have 12 cars." His brother Aiden said, "I have seven."

Elijah said, "Together we have 18!" Aiden said, "That's not right! It's 17."

Who is correct?

4. Connect the problems to the right answer.

| 14 − 9 | | 13 − 9 |
| 12 − 5 | **7** | 14 − 7 |
| 12 − 8 | **5** | 11 − 6 |
| 13 − 8 | **4** | 15 − 8 |

| 12 − 6 | | 14 − 6 |
| 15 − 7 | **9** | 16 − 7 |
| 18 − 9 | **6** | 15 − 9 |
| 16 − 7 | **8** | 13 − 7 |

5. Write the number that the shape represents.

a. $\bigcirc − 5 = 6$

$\bigcirc$ is _____

b. $12 − \square = 6$

$\square$ is _____

c. $\triangle + 7 = 14$

$\triangle$ is _____

6. Compare, writing <, >, or = in the box.

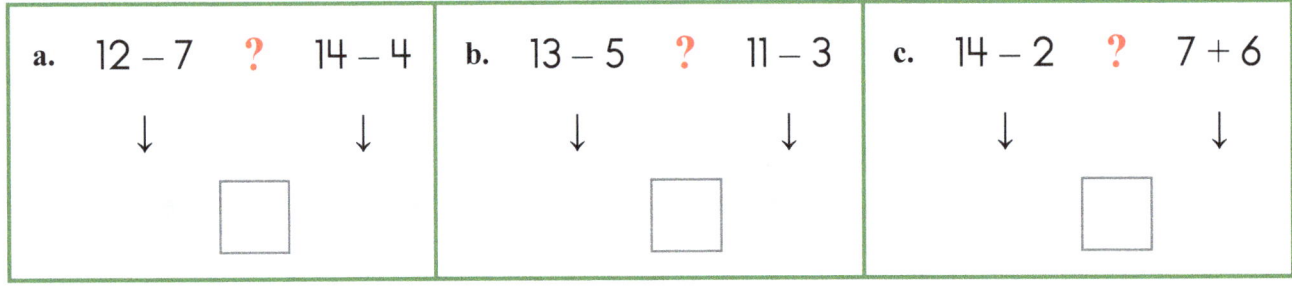

a. $12 − 7$ **?** $14 − 4$
↓ ↓
□

b. $13 − 5$ **?** $11 − 3$
↓ ↓
□

c. $14 − 2$ **?** $7 + 6$
↓ ↓
□

7. Color by numbers. The areas without numbers you can color however you like!

$1 + 4 + 5 =$ light orange

$3 + 4 + 2 =$ brown

$14 − 5 − 1 =$ dark orange

$12 − 3 − 2 =$ light brown

$11 − 1 − 4 =$ red

# Subtract Two-Digit Numbers

We can also subtract two numbers this way: We write the numbers in the grid, and then subtract the tens in their own column, and the ones in their own column. Here, 95 − 22 equals 73.

|  | tens | ones |
|---|---|---|
|  | 9 | 5 |
| − | 2 | 2 |
|  | 7 | 3 |

But sometimes this does not work directly. Note that in subtracting 95 − 26, we cannot subtract in the ones because it has 5 − 6. You cannot take away 6 from 5. You will learn how to deal with this situation in second grade.

|  | tens | ones |
|---|---|---|
|  | 9 | 5 |
| − | 2 | 6 |
|  | ? | ? |

1. Subtract.

**a.**

| tens | ones |
|---|---|
| 9 | 5 |
| − 2 | 0 |
|  |  |

**b.**

| tens | ones |
|---|---|
| 5 | 8 |
| − 2 | 6 |
|  |  |

**c.**

| tens | ones |
|---|---|
| 2 | 5 |
| − 0 | 3 |
|  |  |

**d.**

| tens | ones |
|---|---|
| 7 | 9 |
| − 6 | 4 |
|  |  |

2. Write the numbers in the grid. Subtract the tens and the ones in their columns.

**a.** 57 − 21

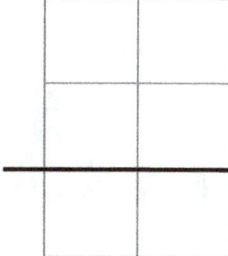

**b.** 74 − 14

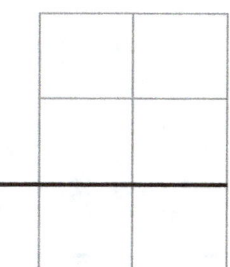

**c.** 59 − 7

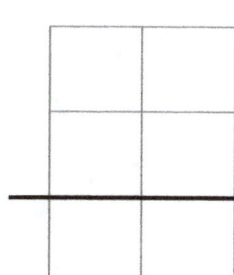

**d.** 99 − 58

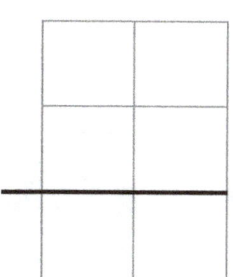

3. (Optional challenge) Use an abacus or drawings to subtract **a.** 43 − 25 **b.** 62 − 38.

4. Subtract. You can cover with your fingers, or cross out, what needs to be subtracted.

| | | |
|---|---|---|
|  a. 48 – 20 = _____ |  b. 47 – 25 = _____ |  c. 61 – 50 = _____ |
|  d. 38 – 14 = _____ | 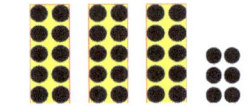 e. 36 – 30 = _____ |  f. 38 – 26 = _____ |

5. Solve. Using the grids is optional.

a. Mom is 38 years old and John is 13.
How many years older is Mom than John?

b. James likes fishing. On Monday, he caught 26 fish. His wife cooked
11 fish for supper and put the rest into the freezer.
On Tuesday, James again went fishing and caught 12 fish.

Make one or more problems from this story, and ask someone else to solve them.

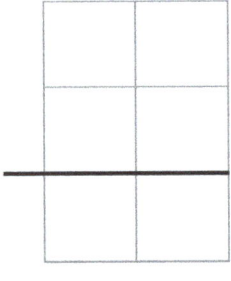 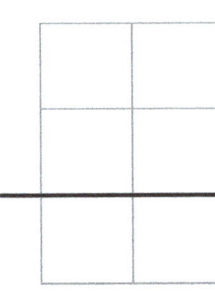 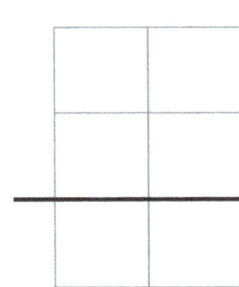

# Add and Subtract Two-Digit Numbers

1. The dots show two numbers to add. Write an addition equation.

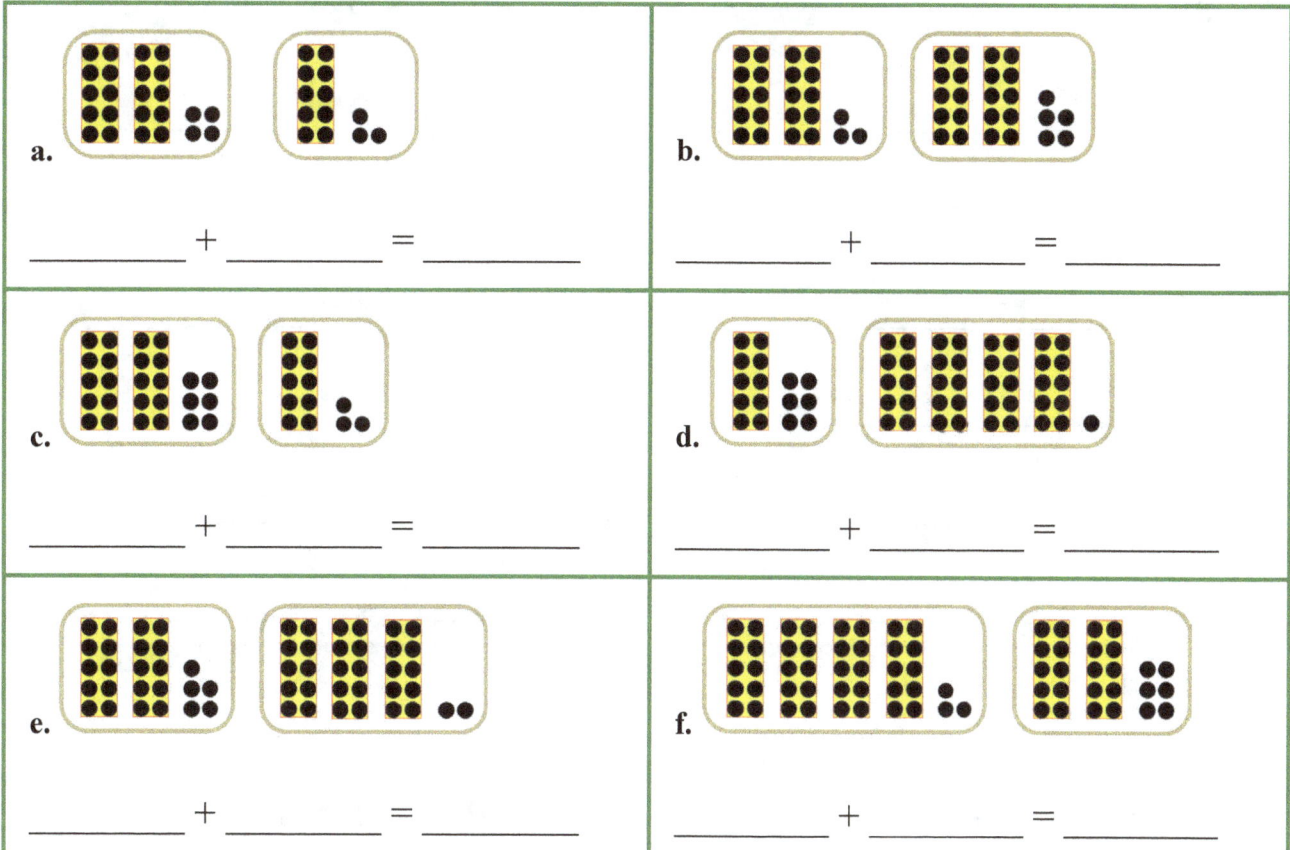

a. _____ + _____ = _____

b. _____ + _____ = _____

c. _____ + _____ = _____

d. _____ + _____ = _____

e. _____ + _____ = _____

f. _____ + _____ = _____

2. Fill in the missing numbers.

| | | |
|---|---|---|
| a. 10 + _____ = 15 | b. 21 + _____ = 22 | c. 65 + _____ = 69 |
| 32 + _____ = 38 | 94 + _____ = 95 | 33 + _____ = 36 |
| 72 + _____ = 79 | 44 + _____ = 48 | 91 + _____ = 98 |

3. Bonnie is 77 years old. How old was she three years ago?

How old will she be in three years?

4. Continue the patterns.

**a.**

$88 - 0 =$ _____

$88 - 1 =$ _____

$88 - 2 =$ _____

$88 -$ ____ $=$ _____

$88 -$ ____ $=$ _____

$88 -$ ____ $=$ _____

$88 -$ ____ $=$ _____

$88 -$ ____ $=$ _____

**b.**

$95 - 2 =$ _____

$85 - 2 =$ _____

$75 - 2 =$ _____

$65 - 2 =$ _____

_____ $- 2 =$ _____

_____ $- 2 =$ _____

_____ $- 2 =$ _____

_____ $- 2 =$ _____

**c.**

$51 + 2 =$ _____

$53 + 2 =$ _____

$55 + 2 =$ _____

_____ $+ 2 =$ _____

_____ $+ 2 =$ _____

_____ $+ 2 =$ _____

_____ $+ 2 =$ _____

_____ $+ 2 =$ _____

**d.**

$48 - 1 =$ _____

$46 - 1 =$ _____

$44 - 1 =$ _____

_____ $- 1 =$ _____

_____ $- 1 =$ _____

_____ $- 1 =$ _____

_____ $- 1 =$ _____

_____ $- 1 =$ _____

**Skip-counting worms!**

The worm above shows a skip-counting pattern by 2s:

3, 5, 7, 9

This worm has a skip-counting pattern by 3s. How is that?

Because each time, you add three:

**2** + 3 = **5**

5 + 3 = **8**

8 + 3 = **11**

11 + 3 = **14**

5. Fill in the missing numbers in these skip-counting worms.

a.

b.

c.

d.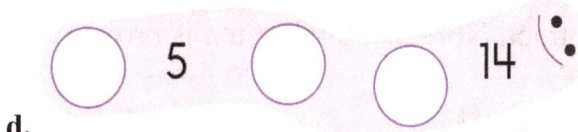

e.

f.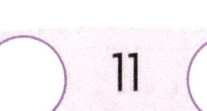

g.

6. A challenge! You may use the 100-bead abacus to help you.

a. 35 + 20 = _____

76 + 30 = _____

b. 33 − 20 = _____

99 − 40 = _____

c. 40 + 17 = _____

56 − 20 = _____

# Subtracting from Whole Tens

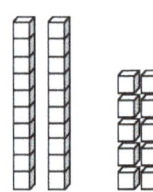

**Example 1:** Subtract 30 – 7.

The picture shows 30 as two ten-columns and ten single blocks.
We can easily subtract (by covering) seven blocks from
the 10 single blocks.

We end up subtracting *from ten*:  10 – 7 = 3.

But since we also have the two other tens, the answer is 23.

**Example 2:** Subtract 50 – 6.

Think of the helping problem where you subtract from ten:  10 – 6 = 4.
The answer ends in *four*.

Now, the answer to 50 – 6 is in the *previous* ten:  in the <u>forties</u>. It is forty-something,
and it ends in four. So the answer is 44.

1. Subtract. Note that the last ten is broken into single blocks.

| | | |
|---|---|---|
| **a.** 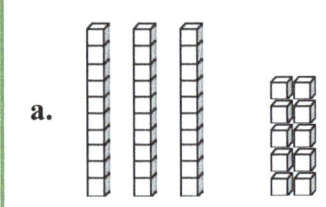 | **b.** 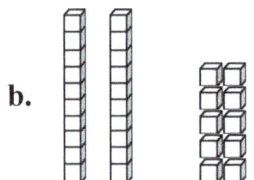 | **c.** 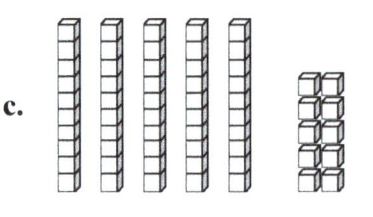 |
| 40 – 4 = _____ | 30 – 5 = _____ | 60 – 7 = _____ |
| 40 – 6 = _____ | 30 – 4 = _____ | 60 – 9 = _____ |
| 40 – 7 = _____ | 30 – 9 = _____ | 60 – 1 = _____ |
| 40 – 8 = _____ | 30 – 6 = _____ | 60 – 4 = _____ |

2. Subtract the same number two times.

| a. | b. | c. |
|---|---|---|
| 50 – 10 – 10 = _____ | 70 – 30 – 30 = _____ | 40 – 20 – 20 = _____ |

3. Subtract.

| a. | b. | c. | d. |
|---|---|---|---|
| $70 - 6 =$ _____ | $50 - 8 =$ _____ | $40 - 1 =$ _____ | $100 - 5 =$ _____ |
| $70 - 5 =$ _____ | $50 - 7 =$ _____ | $40 - 5 =$ _____ | $100 - 4 =$ _____ |
| $70 - 2 =$ _____ | $50 - 3 =$ _____ | $40 - 9 =$ _____ | $100 - 8 =$ _____ |

4. Add and subtract the same number.

a. $10 - 2 =$ _____

$10 + 2 =$ _____

b. $60 - 5 =$ _____

$60 + 5 =$ _____

c. $25 - 4 =$ _____

$25 + 4 =$ _____

5. Solve. Write an addition or subtraction in the pink space, to match the problem.

a. There are 20 pupils in the class, and each one needed a pencil.
The teacher found only 16 pencils.
How many pencils do they still need?

They still need _____ pencils.

b. There are 17 bushes growing in the front yard and seven in the back yard.
How many more are in the front yard than in the back yard?

_____ more in the front yard

c. Maya has 13 pretty stones, Leah has 18, and Chloe has 20.

How many more stones does Chloe have than Maya?

Chloe has _____ more than Maya.

How many more stones does Leah have than Maya?

Leah has _____ more than Maya.

# Chapter 8 Mixed Review

1. Order these things from the shortest to the longest. Write 1 on the shortest object, 2 on the one that is neither the shortest nor the longest, and 3 on the longest.

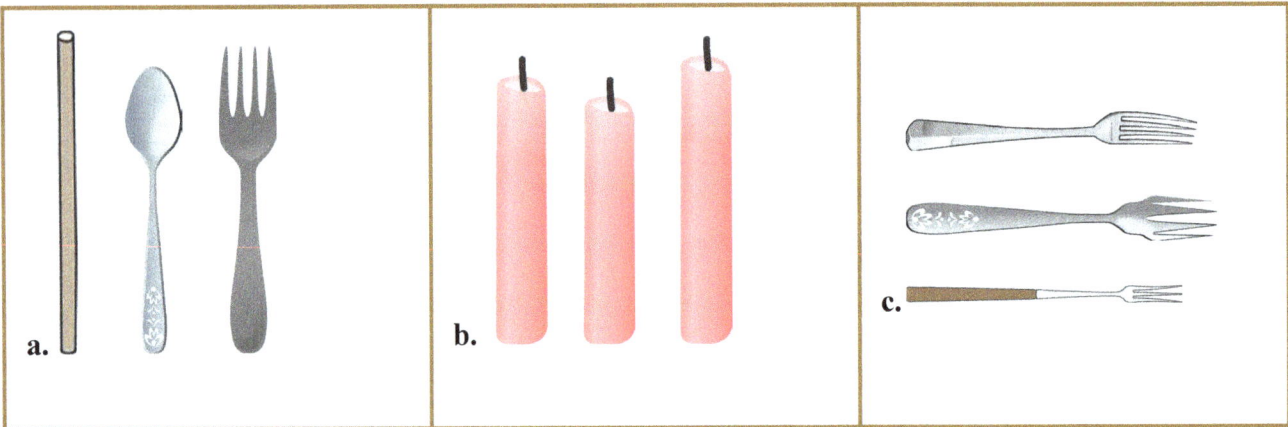

2. Measure these lines with an inch-ruler.

   a. _____ in

   b. _____ in

   c.

   _____ in

3. How many triangles can you find in this figure?

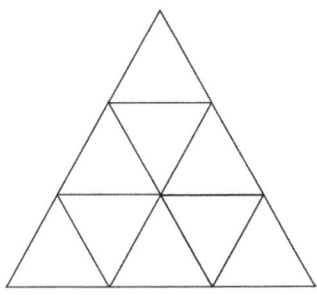

4. First add and subtract. Then compare, and write <, > or =.

| a.  8 – 3  ?  7 – 3 | b.  2 + 5  ?  7 – 1 | c.  10 – 6  ?  3 + 4 |
|---|---|---|
| ↓        ↓ | ↓        ↓ | ↓        ↓ |
| ☐ | ☐ | ☐ |

5. Divide the shape into equal shares. Color. Lastly, name the colored portion (the fraction).

**a.** Divide into two equal shares.
Color one part.

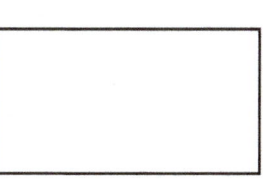

_____

**b.** Divide into four equal shares.
Color 2 parts.

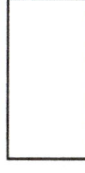

_____

**c.** Divide into four equal shares.
Color 3 parts.

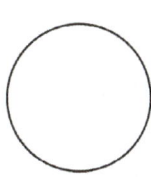

_____

**d.** Divide into two equal shares.
Color 2 parts.

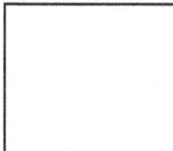

_____

6. Write $<$ , $>$ or $=$ .

**a.** $70 + 2$ ☐ $55$     **b.** $9 + 10$ ☐ $26$     **c.** $78$ ☐ $7 + 80$

7. Which of the given numbers fits the comparison below? Write it on the empty line.

| **a.** 59   81   75 | **b.** 17   18   31 | **c.** 39   99   93 |
|---|---|---|
| _____ $> 76$ | $18 <$ _____ | $45 >$ _____ |

8. Add and subtract.

| **a.** | **b.** | **c.** |
|---|---|---|
| $8 - 2 - 3 =$ _____ | $2 + 4 + 1 =$ _____ | $6 - 2 - 4 =$ _____ |
| $9 - 1 - 6 =$ _____ | $7 + 2 + 1 =$ _____ | $10 - 2 - 6 =$ _____ |

# Chapter 8 Review

1. Solve. Write the letter after each problem in the purple box below the right answer.

| | | |
|---|---|---|
| 60 + _____ = 68  **A** | 90 – 60 = _____  **E** | 8 + 8 = _____  **L** |
| 52 + _____ = 55  **L** | 60 – 8 = _____  **T** | 11 + 5 = _____  **H** |
| 22 + _____ = 27  **O** | 91 – 20 = _____  **M** | 3 + 8 = _____  **O** |
| 11 + _____ = 20  **U** | 32 – 10 = _____  **V** | 30 – 3 = _____  **O** |
| 56 – 6 = _____  **E** | 13 – 6 = _____  **F** | 72 + 6 = _____  **S** |
| 80 – 20 = _____  **L** | 100 – 4 = _____  **Y** | 64 + 6 = _____  **D** |

96    27    9

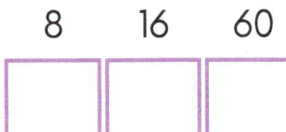 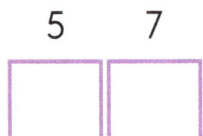 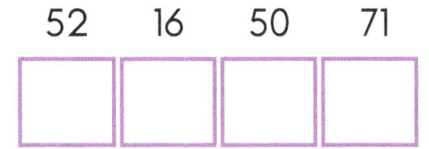

78    11    3    22    30    70

8    16    60

5    7

52    16    50    71

!

2. Write the second number under the first and then add or subtract them.

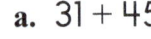

**a.** 31 + 45        **b.** 51 + 8        **c.** 99 – 45        **d.** 47 – 5

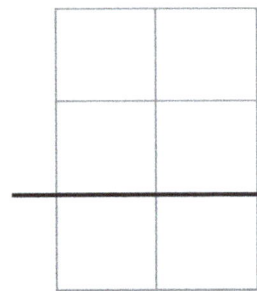  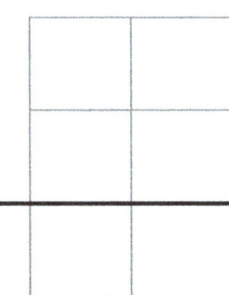 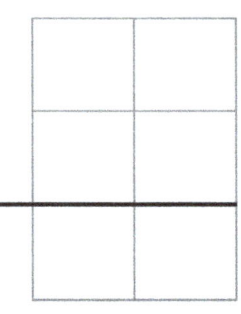

3. **a.** Fill in the doubles chart at the right. Notice that the sums are in scrambled order.

**b.** Use the doubles to help you solve these problems.

$7 + 8 =$ _____     $6 + 7 =$ _____

$6 + 5 =$ _____     $8 + 9 =$ _____

**c.** *Explain* to your teacher or classmate *how* the doubles helped you.

$8 + 8 =$ _____

$6 + 6 =$ _____

$5 + 5 =$ _____

$9 + 9 =$ _____

$7 + 7 =$ _____

4. Add. Tell which idea you use to add.

| Trick with nine | **a.** $9 + 9 =$ _____ | **b.** $8 + 4 =$ _____ | Doubles facts |
| Trick with eight | **c.** $9 + 5 =$ _____ | **d.** $7 + 7 =$ _____ | Just one more than a double |
| "Just one more" than a sum with 10 | **e.** $7 + 8 =$ _____ | **f.** $6 + 5 =$ _____ | I just know it! |
| | **g.** $3 + 9 =$ _____ | **h.** $6 + 7 =$ _____ | |

5. Color by numbers. (Color the spaces without a number however you want to.)

brown = $13 - 6$

red = $17 - 7$

yellow = $13 - 8$

blue = $11 - 5$

pink = $14 - 6$

orange = $13 - 9$

gray = $20 - 8$

light green = $17 - 8$

147

6. Solve.

**a.** Michael had eight books. Then his mom gave him
one more, and dad gave him three more.
How many books does Michael have now?

**b.** Your sister is on page 64 of a 70-page book.
How many pages does she have left to read?

**c.** Sam is 12 years old and Jack is 4.
How many years older is Sam than Jack?

**d.** Camila and Isaiah ate some blueberries. Camila ate 17, which was
three fewer than what Isaiah ate. How many did Isaiah eat?

7. Add. In some of these problems you need to make a new ten with some
of the little dots. You can also use an abacus.

**a.** 15 + 8 = _____

**b.** 37 + 9 = _____

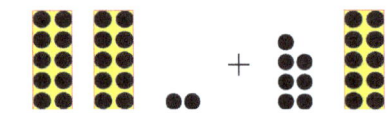

**c.** 24 + 14 = _____

**d.** 22 + 17 = _____

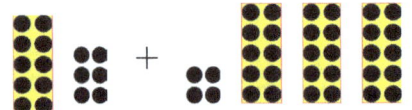

**e.** 16 + 34 = _____

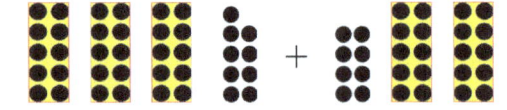

**f.** 39 + 28 = _____

8. Subtract. You can subtract in parts or think of addition.

| | | |
|---|---|---|
| **a.** 11 − 2 = _____ | **b.** 12 − 4 = _____ | **c.** 13 − 5 = _____ |
| 11 − 4 = _____ | 12 − 5 = _____ | 13 − 7 = _____ |
| 11 − 5 = _____ | 12 − 6 = _____ | 13 − 4 = _____ |

9. Correct or not? Cross out the equations that are false.

**a.** 13 − 7 = 6        **b.** 8 = 16 − 9        **c.** 5 + 8 = 6 + 7        **d.** 15 − 7 = 7

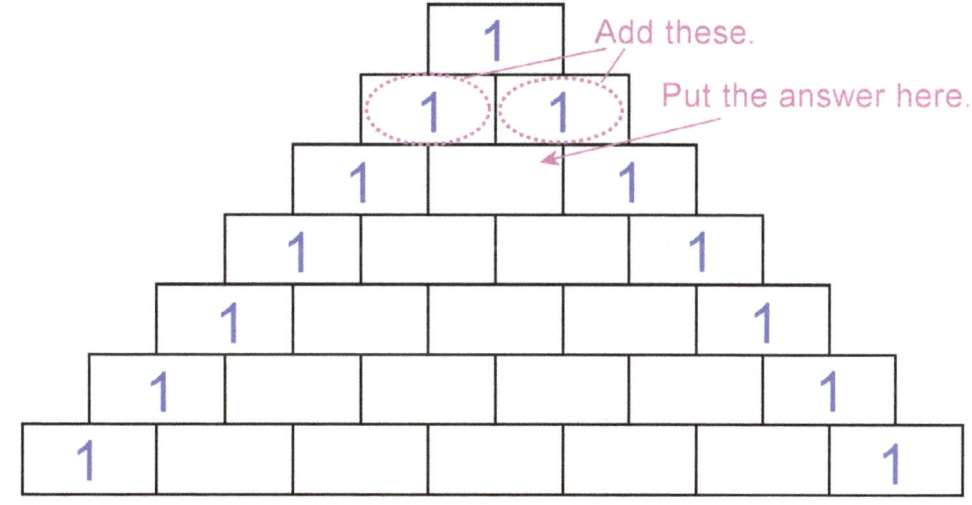

**Puzzle Corner**   Pyramid numbers. Add two numbers that are next to each other, and put the sum *below* them both, in the middle.

Add these.

Put the answer here.

149

# Chapter 9: Graphs
## Introduction

This is a short chapter, focusing on bar graphs. There is also one optional lesson on tally marks. In Kindergarten, children have sorted items into categories, and sorted the categories by count, preparing them for what we do here in first grade. Now, the goals are that the child is able to...

- organize data into three categories;

- make a bar graph (or a tally) to represent the data;

- ask and answer simple questions about the data and the graph.

The lessons are fairly simple and introductory, helping children to get started organizing data and understanding how we can represent data with a graph.

In second grade, students work with both picture graphs (pictographs) and bar graphs, with single-unit scale when the data has up to four categories. Then in third grade, students continue with *scaled* bar graphs and pictographs; in other words, each picture in the pictograph or each "block" in the bar graph represents more than one thing.


## Pacing Suggestion for Chapter 9

Please add one day to the pacing for the test if you will use it.

| The Lessons in Chapter 9 | page | span | suggested pacing | your pacing |
|---|---|---|---|---|
| Bar Graphs ........................................................ | 153 | 3 pages | 1 day | |
| More Bar Graphs ............................................... | 156 | 2 pages | 1 day | |
| More Practice with Graphs ............................. | 158 | 2 pages | 1 day | |
| Tally Marks (optional) ..................................... | 160 | 2 pages | 1 day | |
| Chapter 9 Mixed Review ................................. | 162 | 2 pages | 1 day | |
| Chapter 9 Review ............................................. | 164 | 2 pages | 1 day | |
| Chapter 9 Test (optional) ................................ | | | | |
| **TOTALS** | | *11 pages* | 5 days | |
| with optional content | | *(13 pages)* | (6 days) | |

# Games and Activities

## Tally Marks

**You need:** Paper, pencil, and things to count where the counting happens over time, not instantly.

Tally marks are most useful for counting things that are happening rather slowly, for example, birds that fly into the yard. For this activity, count something using tally marks. Ideally, you will count three different things. For example, you could count how many blue, black, and gray cars you see pass by your house in 20 minutes. Or you could count how many men, women, and children pass by your house in some time frame. Or you could count three different kinds of birds.

For each kind of thing, you will use tally marks to make a count. Write each kind of thing you count on a separate line on your paper, and then make a row of tally marks for that thing.

## Further Resources on the Internet

These resources match the topics in this chapter, and offer online practice, online games (occasionally, printable games), and interactive illustrations of math concepts. We heartily recommend you take a look. Many people love using these resources to supplement the bookwork, to illustrate a concept better, and for some fun. Enjoy!

https://l.mathmammoth.com/2026/gr1ch9

# Bar Graphs

This is a **bar graph**. It shows how many roses, petunias, and sunflowers Amanda has in her flower bed. Each block or square means one flower.

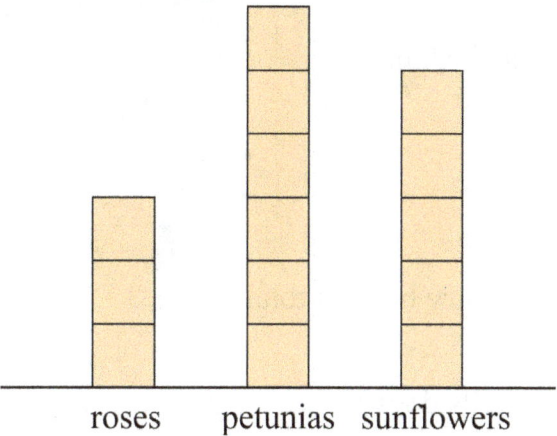

How many sunflowers does she have?          How many petunias?

The graph below shows the same information. Now, instead of individual blocks or squares, we have rectangles. There is also a number line, called an **axis**. We can call it the vertical axis ("vertical" refers to its up-down direction) or the numerical axis (since it has numbers).

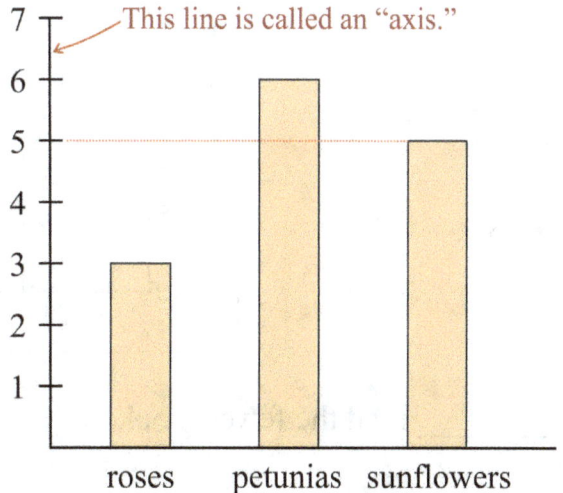

To read the graph, check how high (to which number) the top of each rectangle reaches. The rectangle for sunflowers reaches up to 5. She has five sunflowers.

How many roses does Amanda have?

1. This bar graph shows how many short pencils, medium-long pencils, and long pencils Henry has.

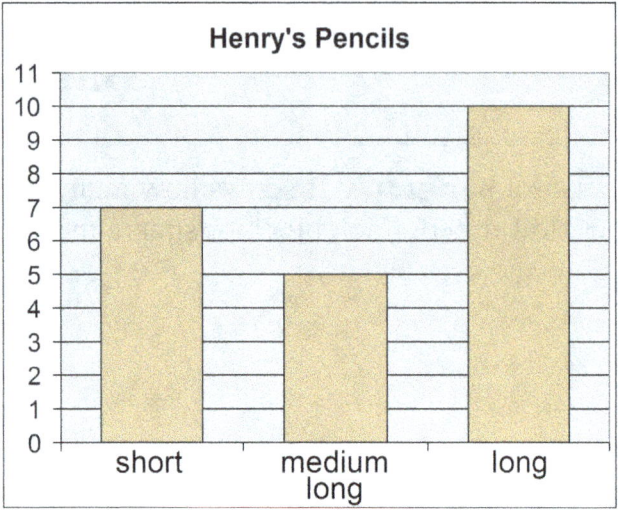

**a.** Fill in:

Henry has _____ short pencils,

_____ medium-long pencils, and

_____ long pencils.

**b.** How many pencils does Henry have in total?

**c.** How many more long pencils does he have than short ones?

2. **a.** How many books did each child read?

Emilia _____    Liam _____

Sara _____

**b.** Liam read _____ more books than Sara.

**c.** Sara read _____ fewer books than Emilia.

**d.** _____ read the fewest books.

_____ read the most books.

**e.** How many books did Emilia and Sara read in total? _____ books

**f.** How many books in total did all three children read? _____ books

3. These are the toys that Zach and Mary have.

**a.** How many dolls do the children have?

**b.** How many teddy bears?

**c.** How many other toys?

Zach and Mary want to make a graph of their toys. To complete the graph, draw one block for each toy. Draw them all the same size and lined up in a column, just like the ones for the dolls.

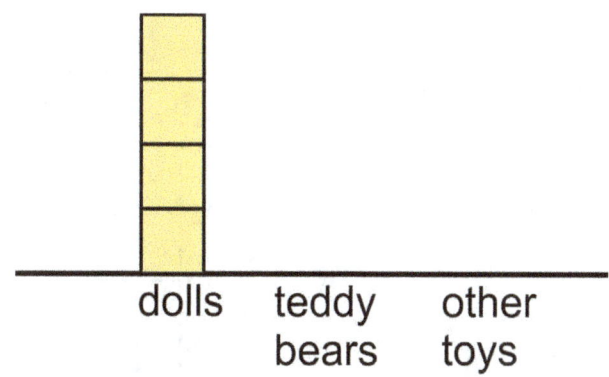

**c.** How many more teddy bears do they have than dolls?

**e.** How many more teddy bears do they have than other toys?

**f.** How many dolls and teddy bears do the children have in all?

# More Bar Graphs

1. Here, the bar for first grade students reaches the line between 8 and 10. That's 9 students.

   **a.** How many students are in 3rd grade?

   **b.** How many students are in 4th grade?

   **c.** How many students are in 1st and 2nd grades, in total?

   **d.** Make your own question about the graph!

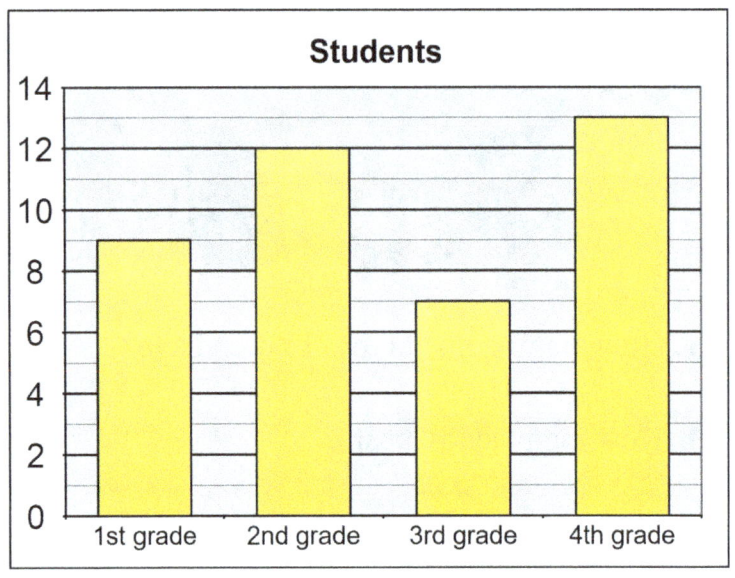

2. **a.** Make a bar graph by drawing a bar for each month in the image.

   | Month | Rainy days |
   |-----------|------------|
   | August | 7 |
   | September | 12 |
   | October | 13 |

   **b.** How many more rainy days did October have than September?

   **c.** How many more rainy days did October have than August?

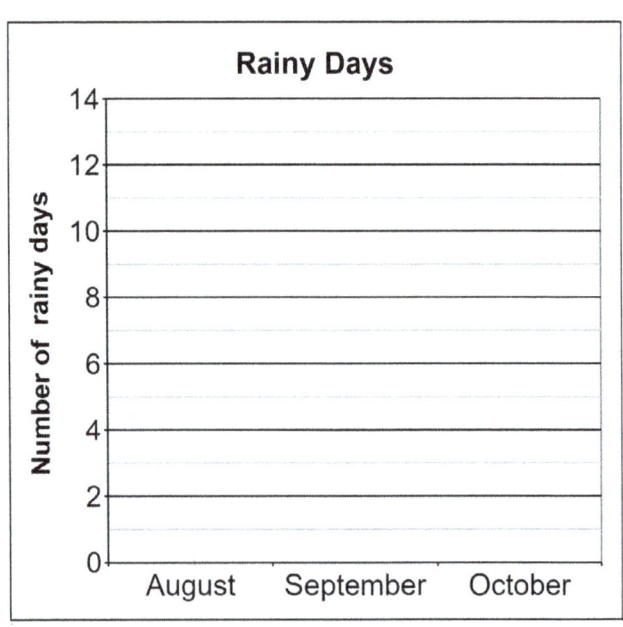

3. Draw a bar graph to show the count of each kind of shape (circles, triangles, squares). You will also need to label the bars in the image.

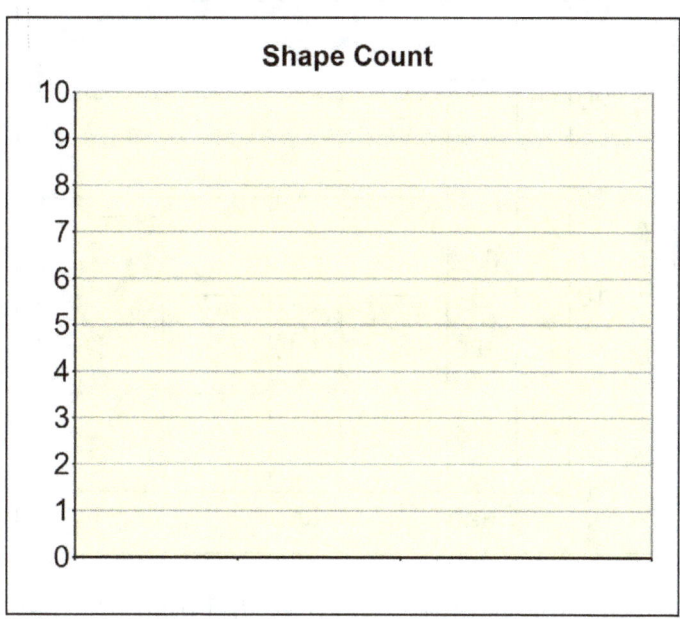

4. Here you see how many coins Mia, Kai, and Mateo have.

a. Make a bar graph.

b. Make your own question about the graph, and answer it.

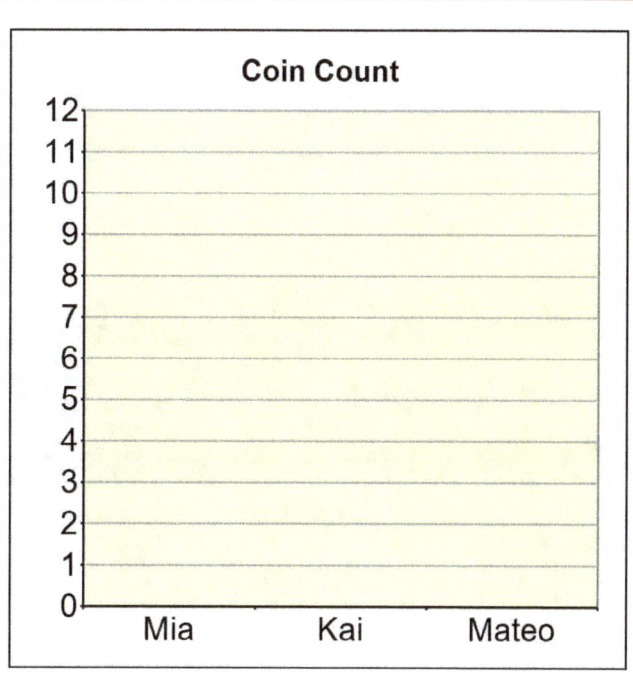

# More Practice with Graphs

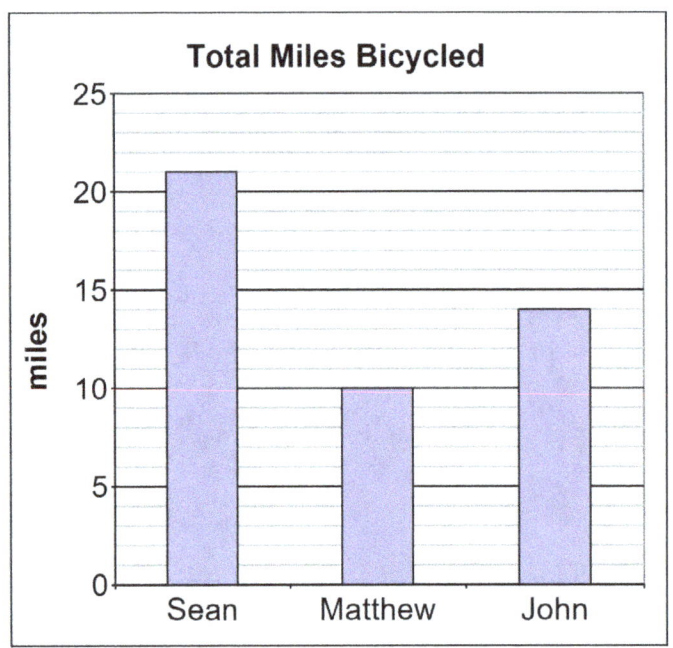

1. Erica calculated how many more miles Sean bicycled than Matthew.
   She got $22 - 10 = 12$ more miles. Is that correct? If not, correct her answer.

2. Write two questions that you could ask another student about the graph in question 1.
   Then, ask your classmate or a friend the questions. Check their answers.

3. **Activity.** Your teacher will give you a bunch of things. They are of three different kinds. Count each kind, and make a bar graph of the counts.

Examples include: teaspoons, tablespoons, and regular spoons; beans, rocks, and counters; counters of three different colors; etc.

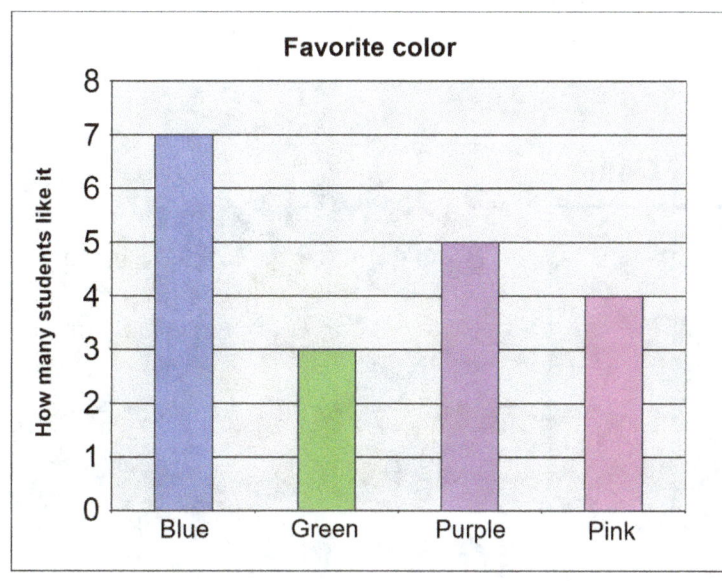

4. Answer.

   **a.** There are _____ students whose favorite color is purple.

   **b.** There are _____ students whose favorite color is blue.

   **c.** How many fewer students like green than like pink?

     _____

   **d.** How many more students like blue than like pink?

     _____

# Tally Marks
## (This lesson is optional.)

1. **Tally marks.** Tally marks are counting marks. When people count, they make one tally mark for each thing they count. For one item or thing, draw one tally mark as "|".
The fifth tally mark is drawn across the four others like this: ⊥⊥⊤.

   Write the number that matches the tally.

| ⊥⊥⊤ \| | ⊥⊥⊤ ⊥⊥⊤ \|\| | ⊥⊥⊤ ⊥⊥⊤ ⊥⊥⊤ \|\|\|\| | ⊥⊥⊤ ⊥⊥⊤ ⊥⊥⊤ ⊥⊥⊤ \|\|\| |
|---|---|---|---|
| **a.** _____ | **b.** _____ | **c.** _____ | **d.** _____ |

2. Draw tally marks for these numbers.

| | |
|---|---|
| **a.** 7 | **b.** 14 |
| **c.** 16 | **d.** 32 |
| **e.** 41 | **f.** 28 |

3. Count the fish. Use tally marks to keep track. Mark each fish you count and make a tally mark for it. That way you won't count the same fish twice. Then write the number under "Count".

| | Tally Marks | Count |
|---|---|---|
| **Red** | | |
| **Blue** | | |
| **Yellow** | | |

4. Count the pencils in each group. Use tally marks to keep track. Mark each pencil as you count it, and make a tally mark in the box. That way you won't count the same pencil twice.

GROUP 1:

GROUP 2:

|  | Tally Marks | Count |
|---|---|---|
| Group 1 |  |  |
| Group 2 |  |  |

5. Do the tally marks show the same counts that the bar graph does? If not, correct the tally.

| | Tally Marks |
|---|---|
| Blue | ̷̷̷̷̷̷̷̷ ̷̷̷̷̷ ̷̷̷̷̷ ̷̷̷̷̷ ̷̷̷̷̷ ‖ |
| Black | ̷̷̷̷̷ ̷̷̷̷̷ |
| White | ̷̷̷̷̷ ̷̷̷̷̷ ̷̷̷̷̷ ̷̷̷̷̷ ‖ |
| Red | ̷̷̷̷̷ ̷̷̷̷̷ ̷̷̷̷̷ |

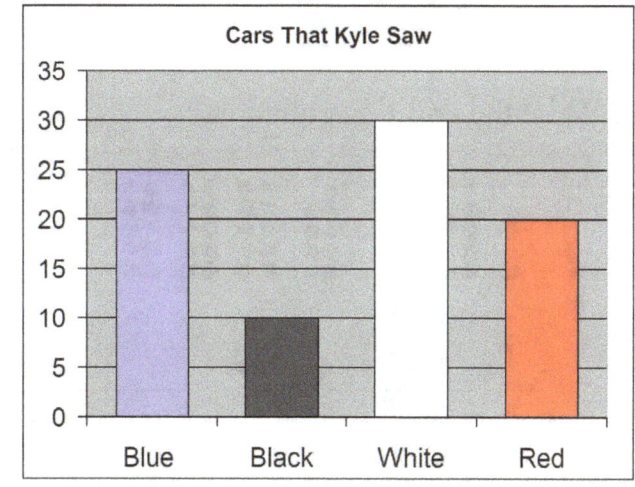

6. (Optional) Tally marks are most useful for counting things that are happening rather slowly, for example, birds that fly into the yard. For this project, count something using tally marks. For example, you could go outside and count how many red and how many gray cars you see pass by your house in 20 minutes.

|  | Tally Marks | Count |
|---|---|---|
| Group 1 |  |  |
| Group 2 |  |  |

# Chapter 9 Mixed Review

1. **Activity.** You will need a set of geometric solids. Use the solids to build the shape on the right.

2. Name the basic solid(s) in these objects.

   a.             b.             c.

3. Add. First make a new ten with some of the single dots. You can also use the abacus.

a.  24  +  17 = _____

b.  38  +  28 = _____

4. Write the addition equation.

a.  _____ + _____ = _____

b.  _____ + _____ = _____

5. Solve.

   **a.** James's chicken was sitting on 14 eggs! But
       later he found that three of them were not good.
       How many eggs were good?

   **b.** Luna counted seven oak trees on one side
       of the driveway, and eight on the other side.
       How many oak trees were lining
       the driveway in total?

6. Find what number the symbol stands for.

| a. 32 + ◯ = 37 | b. 88 − ◯ = 81 | c. 60 − ● = 52 |
|---|---|---|
| ◯ = _____ | ◯ = _____ | ● = _____ |

7. Below each doubles fact write a sum that is "just one more."

| a. 5 + 5 = _____ | b. 7 + 7 = _____ | c. 8 + 8 = _____ |
|---|---|---|
| ____ + ____ = _____ | ____ + ____ = _____ | ____ + ____ = _____ |

8. Write the time a half-hour later. Use numbers.

| Now it is: | a. 2:00 | b. 12:00 | c. 7:30 | d. 10:30 |
|---|---|---|---|---|
| A half-hour later, it is: | | | | |

9. Continue the patterns.

| a. | b. | c. |
|---|---|---|
| 100 − 1 = _____ | 10 − 1 = _____ | 10 + 90 = _____ |
| 90 − 2 = _____ | 20 − 2 = _____ | 20 + 80 = _____ |
| 80 − 3 = _____ | 30 − 3 = _____ | 30 + 70 = _____ |
| ____ − ____ = _____ | ____ − ____ = _____ | ____ + ____ = _____ |
| ____ − ____ = _____ | ____ − ____ = _____ | ____ + ____ = _____ |
| ____ − ____ = _____ | ____ − ____ = _____ | ____ + ____ = _____ |
| ____ − ____ = _____ | ____ − ____ = _____ | ____ + ____ = _____ |

# Chapter 9 Review

1. Three girls counted how many dolls they had.

    **a.** Draw a bar graph.

    **b.** How many dolls do the girls have in total?

| Girl | Dolls |
|------|-------|
| Maggie | 11 |
| Lily | 6 |
| Susana | 8 |

2. Make up two other questions about the graph in #1. Write the questions below. Then, ask someone else the questions. Remember to check their answers!

    Question 1: _____

    _____

    Answer 1: _____

    Question 2: _____

    _____

    Answer 2: _____

3. Lily took out all the spoons, forks, and knives in the kitchen drawer. Here is what she got:

Make a bar graph, showing the total count of the spoons, forks, and knives.

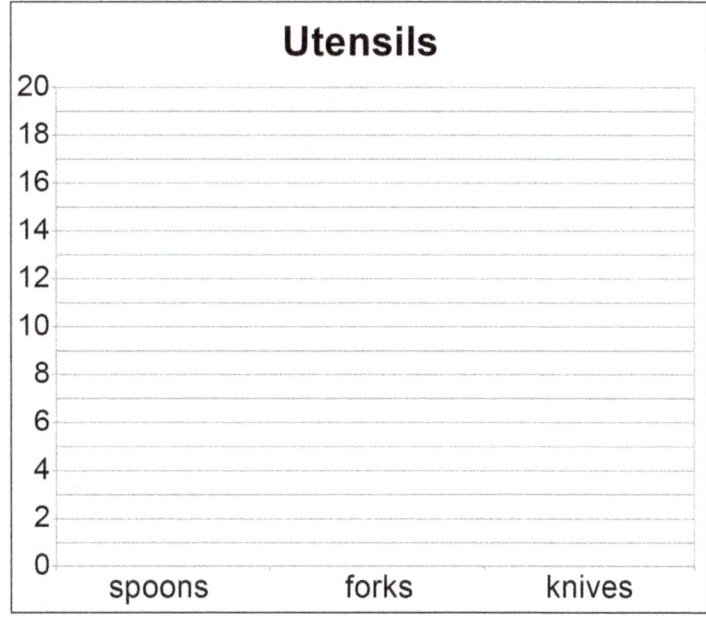

4. (optional) The family made a tally of how many birds they saw on their trip.

| | | Count | |
|---|---|---|---|
| **Dad** | ЖЖ ЖЖ ЖЖ \|\|\|\| | | |
| **Mom** | | | |
| **Mary** | | | |

a. Mom saw 23 birds, and Mary saw 12. Draw the tally marks in the table.

b. How many more birds did Dad see than Mary?

c. How many fewer birds did Dad see than Mom?

# Chapter 10: Coins
## Introduction

In this last chapter, we study counting coins. The goals are that the student learns to identify and count pennies, nickels, dimes, and quarters, when the amounts are 100 cents at most.

In the first lesson, we start out by counting only dimes and pennies, which is identical to practicing place value with tens and ones. The same lesson introduces the nickel.

Next, we practice counting pennies, nickels, and dimes for two lessons. The following lesson then introduces the quarter. First, we practice counting only quarters and dimes, then quarters and nickels, and lastly all the coins. If counting quarters is difficult for your student, you can delay this topic till second grade.

The Common Core Standards (CCS) do not include anything about money or coins for first grade, so if you are following the CCS precisely, or if time does not allow, you can safely use this content (or some of it) in second grade. In second grade, students practice counting coins and solve simple word problems that involve dollar bills, quarters, dimes, nickels, and pennies, using $ and ¢ symbols appropriately.

Note 1: If you have the grayscale version of the book, or have printed in grayscale, it is helpful to color the pennies orange before doing the exercises.

Note 2: At the time of this writing, the U.S. has discontinued minting the penny; however it continues in circulation, so we have decided to continue including the penny in the lessons.

## Pacing Suggestion for Chapter 10

Please add one day to the pacing for the test if you will use it.

| The Lessons in Chapter 10 | page | span | suggested pacing | your pacing |
|---|---|---|---|---|
| Counting Dimes, Nickels, and Pennies 1 ..................... | 170 | *2 pages* | 1 day | |
| Counting Dimes, Nickels, and Pennies 2 ..................... | 172 | *2 pages* | 1 day | |
| More about Coins .................................................. | 174 | *2 pages* | 1 day | |
| Quarters, Part 1 .................................................... | 176 | *2 pages* | 1 day | |
| Quarters, Part 2 .................................................... | 178 | *2 pages* | 1 day | |
| Practicing with Money ............................................ | 180 | *2 pages* | 1 day | |
| Chapter 10 Mixed Review ....................................... | 182 | *5 pages* | 2 days | |
| Chapter 10 Review ................................................. | 187 | *1 page* | 1 day | |
| Chapter 10 Test (optional) | | | | |
| **TOTALS** | | *18 pages* | 9 days | |

# Games and Activities

## Counting Money

**You need:** A bunch of coins (real or fake) to count.

Give the child an amount to make with the coins, such as 14 cents. Once the child does so, it is their turn to give you a money amount to make with the coins.

Start out with only pennies and dimes (they are the easiest to count). Then add the nickel. Instruct the child to count two nickels as a ten. The quarter is the most difficult of the coins. When introducing it, first teach the child that two quarters is 50 cents, three quarters is 75 cents, and four quarters is 100 cents. After that, you can go on to mixtures of quarters and other coins (step-by-step!).

**Note:** You can ask the child to check your work, and then in turn, you check theirs. In the course of the activity, you can then sometimes make an intentional error, so that the child can discover it.

## Shopping Game

**You need:** Various items to purchase at the store, paper, pen, coins, a bag or wallet to keep money in.

Make a play store that has various items to purchase. The prices need to be less than one dollar. The child or student may enjoy choosing prices, and/or writing price tags for them. Typically, it is best if the teacher is the storekeeper, at least in the beginning.

In first grade, children may not understand about change, so at first, the idea is that the child will shop in the store, and pay with exact change. However, with time you might be able to introduce the idea of paying with a larger coin than what the item costs, and receiving change as the difference between what the item costs and what the customer pays.

Some children may enjoy it if the storekeeper writes a receipt for every purchase. After a while, you might switch roles and let the child be a storekeeper (and possibly write receipts). All of my children enjoyed this activity very much.

# Games and Activities at Math Mammoth Practice Zone

### Shopping Game
Practice making money amounts with coins and bills in this online game. You're shown an item to buy, and you click on coins/bills to make that exact amount.
https://www.mathmammoth.com/practice/shopping-game

### Counting Money Game
Practice counting coins and bills in this online game! You can choose the exact coins and bills to use, the maximum for the total amount, the maximum number of coins/bills, and more. This allows you to make the activity as easy or difficult as desired.
https://www.mathmammoth.com/practice/count-money

## Further Resources on the Internet

These resources match the topics in this chapter, and offer online practice, online games (occasionally, printable games), and interactive illustrations of math concepts. We heartily recommend you take a look. Many people love using these resources to supplement the bookwork, to illustrate a concept better, and for some fun. Enjoy!

https://l.mathmammoth.com/2026/gr1ch10

# Counting Dimes, Nickels, and Pennies 1

|   front   back | This coin is a **penny**. It is worth <u>1 cent</u>.<br><br>We write 1¢. |   front   back | This coin is called a **dime**. It is worth <u>ten cents</u>.<br><br>We write 10¢. |
|---|---|---|---|

**Count up** to find how many cents there are in total. Start with the dimes.

  10¢    20¢    21¢    22¢    23¢    24¢

Two dimes is 20¢.
Four pennies is 4¢.
The total is 24 cents.

1. Count and write the total amount in cents.

a.      _____¢

b.        _____¢

c.           _____¢

d.             _____¢

e.   _____¢

  This coin is a **nickel**. It is worth five cents (5¢).

front     back

 These are small pictures of nickels.

Count up from the biggest coins to find the total. Below, the total is bolded.

Count up →  5¢  **6¢**

Count up →  5¢  10¢  11¢  **12¢**

10¢  20¢  **25¢**

2. These are nickels (5¢) and pennies (1¢). Find the total value in cents.

a. _____¢

b. _____¢

c. _____¢

d. _____¢

3. These are dimes (10¢) and nickels (5¢). Find the total value in cents.

a. _____¢

b. _____¢

c. _____¢

d. _____¢

4. Make these amounts of money. You can use real or play money, or draw gray circles with "10" for dimes and orange circles with "1" for pennies. (Using nickels is optional.)

| a. 12¢ | b. 40¢ |
|---|---|
| c. 24¢ | d. 31¢ |

# Counting Dimes, Nickels, and Pennies 2

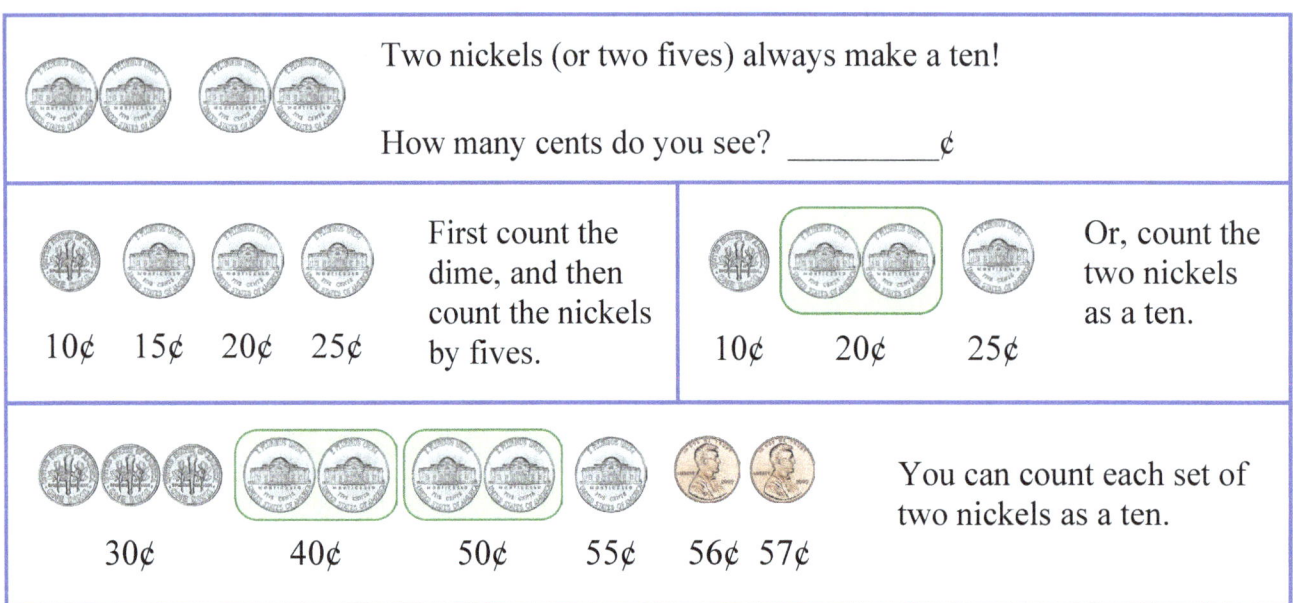

Two nickels (or two fives) always make a ten!

How many cents do you see? _____ ¢

First count the dime, and then count the nickels by fives.

10¢  15¢  20¢  25¢

Or, count the two nickels as a ten.

10¢  20¢  25¢

You can count each set of two nickels as a ten.

30¢     40¢     50¢     55¢  56¢ 57¢

1. **Activity** (optional). You will need: a bunch of dimes and nickels (can be real or play money). Work in pairs. Person 1 chooses some dimes and nickels and gives them to Person 2 to count. Person 2 finds the total value in cents, and then Person 1 checks their work. Then, switch roles.

   Do this activity also with nickels and pennies, and lastly with all three types of coins.

2. Write the total amount in cents. <u>Note:</u> Dimes and nickels are sometimes hard to tell apart. A dime is a little *smaller* in size, but is worth more!

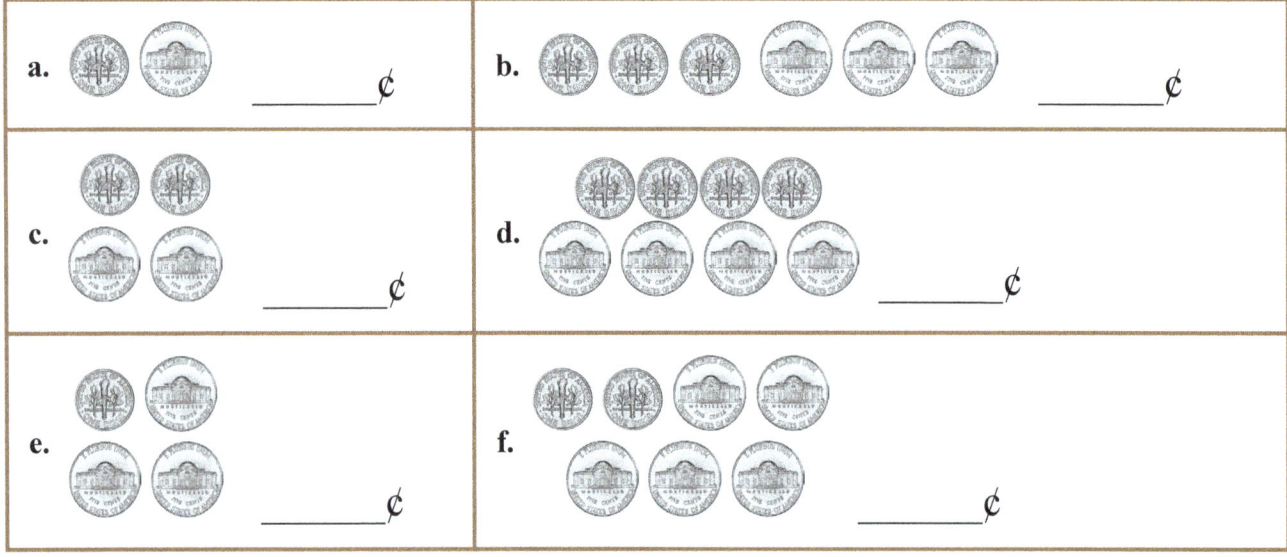

a. _____ ¢

b. _____ ¢

c. _____ ¢

d. _____ ¢

e. _____ ¢

f. _____ ¢

3. Write the total amount in cents.

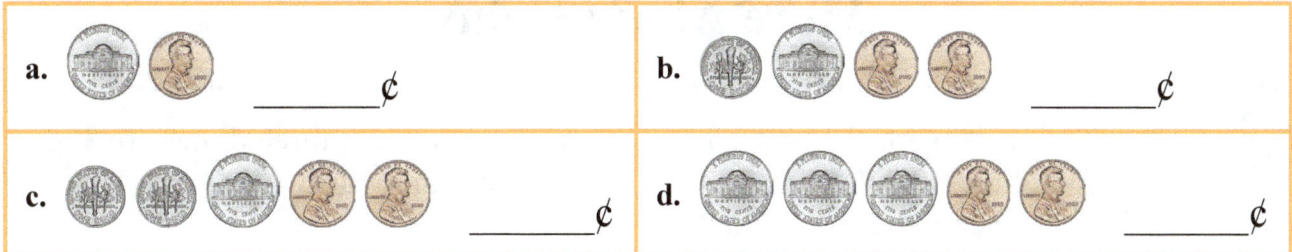

4. Draw one dime more — how much money is there now?

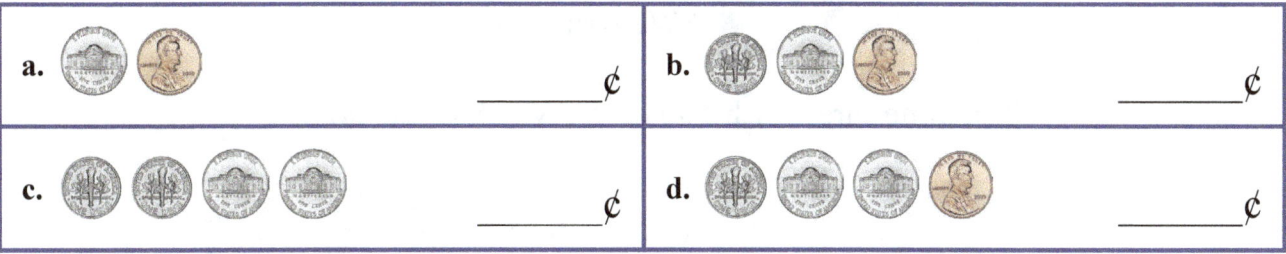

5. Draw one nickel more — how much money now?

| a. | _____ ¢ | b. | _____ ¢ |
| c. | _____ ¢ | d. | _____ ¢ |

6. Make these amounts with real or play money, or draw. Draw gray circles with "10" for dimes, gray circles with "5" for nickels, and orange circles with "1" for pennies.

| a.  25¢ | b. 39¢ | c. 14¢ |
|---------|--------|--------|
| d. 38¢ | e. 63¢ | f. 16¢ |

# More About Coins

 A dime is worth 10 cents. Two dimes are worth 20¢, three dimes are 30¢, four dimes are 40¢, and so on, until 10 dimes are worth 100¢. And a hundred cents makes **one dollar**!

 This is a one-dollar bill.

We write one dollar as **$1**.

Ten dimes are worth 100 cents, which is one dollar:

 = 100¢ = $1 =

1. Since a penny ( 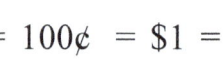 ) is worth 1¢, how many pennies does it take to make one dollar?

2. **a.** How many nickels ( = 5¢) do you need to make 10 cents?

   **b.** How many nickels do you need to make 20 cents?

   **c.** How many nickels do you need to make 30 cents?

   **d.** How many nickels do you need to make 1 dollar?

3. Add more coins to make the given amount. Draw gray circles with "10" for dimes, gray circles with "5" for nickels, and orange circles with "1" for pennies.

| a. 61¢ | b. 45¢ | c. 27¢ |
|---|---|---|
|  |  |  |

4. Cross out the coins you need to buy the item. Write how many cents you have left.

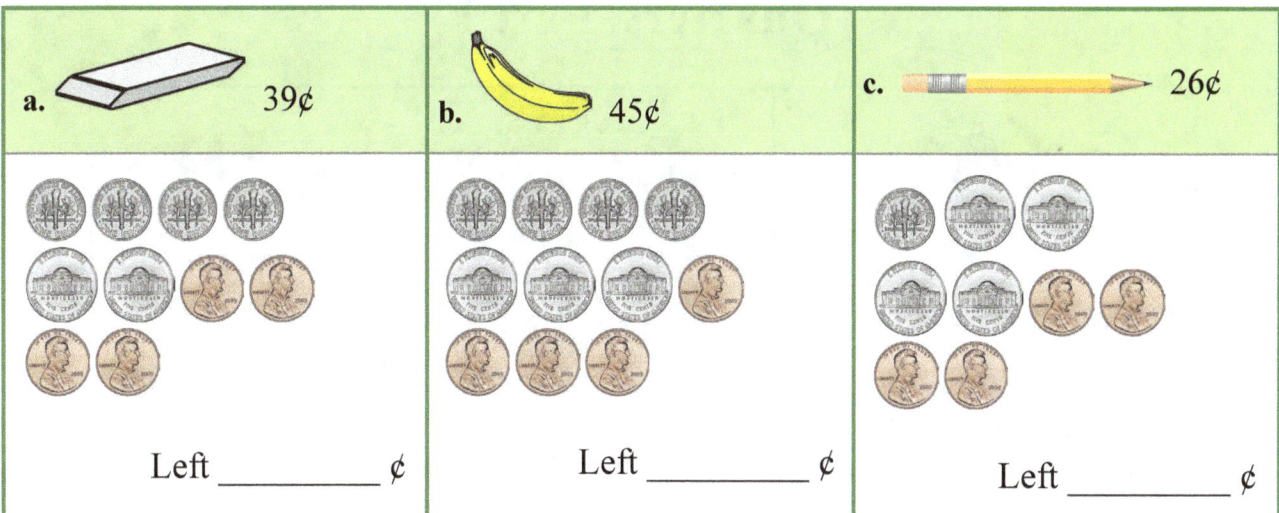

a. 39¢

Left _____ ¢

b. 45¢

Left _____ ¢

c. 26¢

Left _____ ¢

5. Write the total amount in cents.

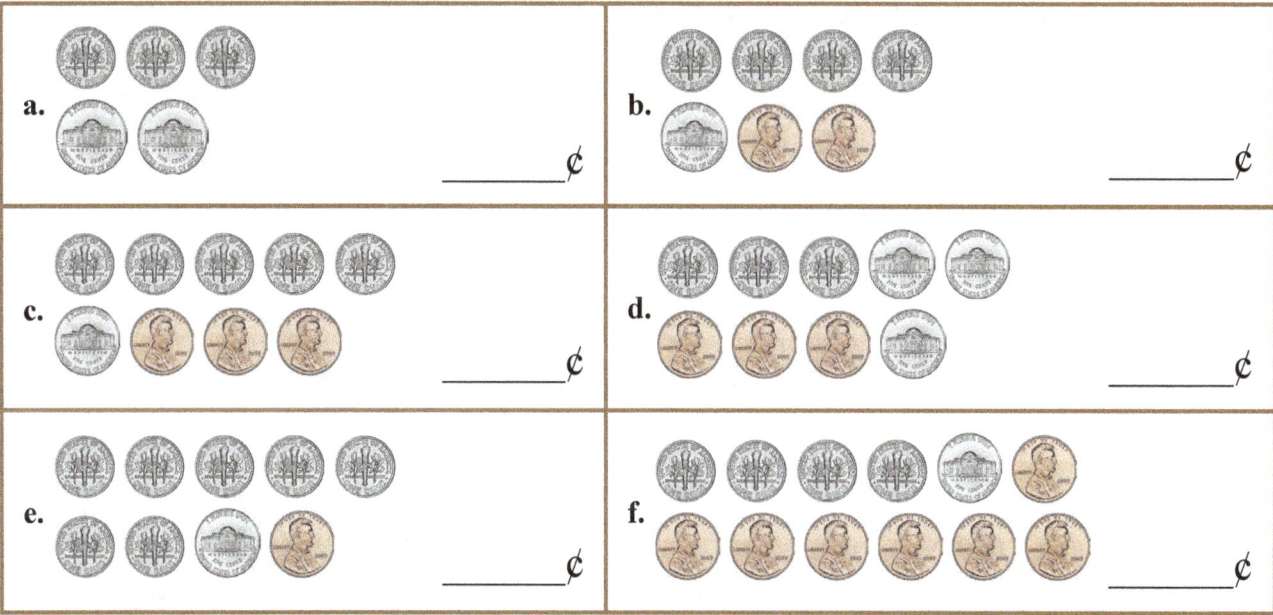

a. _____ ¢

b. _____ ¢

c. _____ ¢

d. _____ ¢

e. _____ ¢

f. _____ ¢

6. You have some money, and then you get some more. How much do you have now?

a.

10¢ + 10¢ = _____ ¢

11¢ + 10¢ = _____ ¢

13¢ + 10¢ = _____ ¢

15¢ + 10¢ = _____ ¢

b.

24¢ + 5¢ = _____ ¢

25¢ + 5¢ = _____ ¢

20¢ + 5¢ = _____ ¢

27¢ + 5¢ = _____ ¢

c.

40¢ + 20¢ = _____ ¢

53¢ + 10¢ = _____ ¢

55¢ + 5¢ = _____ ¢

56¢ + 20¢ = _____ ¢

# Quarters, Part 1

One **quarter** is 25 cents.

The word "quarter" means one-fourth. A quarter coin is one-fourth part of a dollar. (One dollar is 100 cents.)

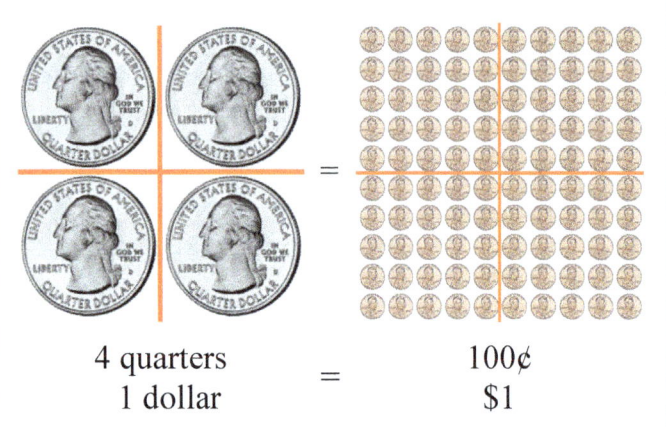

4 quarters   =   100¢
1 dollar          $1

1. What is the total value, in cents, of two quarters?

   (Hint: to add 25 and 25, first add 20 + 20, and 5 + 5. Lastly add those two sums.)

2. What is the total value, in cents, of three quarters?

3. Quarters and dimes. Write the total amount in cents.

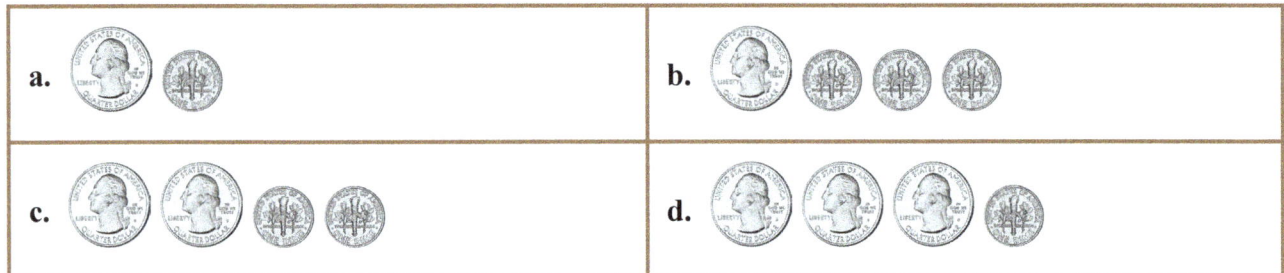

4. Quarters and nickels. Write the total amount in cents. (Hint: two nickels make 10¢.)

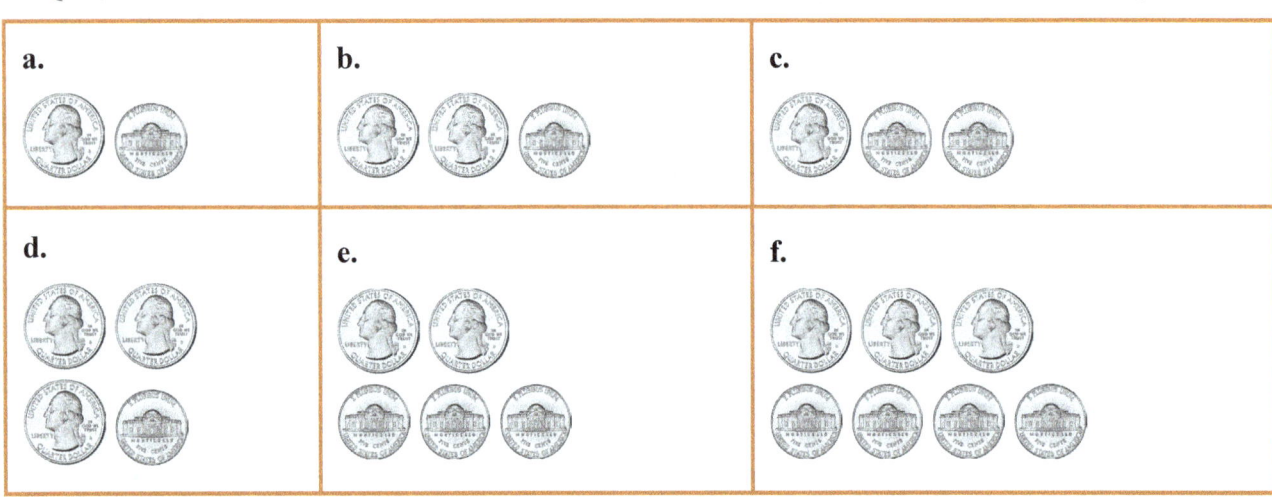

25¢     35, 45     55¢     Count the quarter(s) first since they have the biggest cent-value. Then add the dimes.

(count dimes by tens)

5. One quarter, dimes, and nickels. Write the total. (Hint: two nickels make 10¢.)

| | |
|---|---|
| a.   | b.     |
| c.     | d.        |

6. Draw more coins to make the given amount.

| a. 40¢ | b. 65¢ | c. 35¢ |
|---|---|---|
|  |  |  |

7. Quarters, dimes, and nickels. Write the total. (Hint: two nickels make 10¢.)

| | |
|---|---|
| a.   | b.   |
| c.  | d.  |

8. Draw more coins to make the given amount.

| a. 60¢ | b. 85¢ | c. 90¢ |
|---|---|---|
|  |  |   |

# Quarters, Part 2

25¢          35, 45, 55          56, 57¢
(count dimes by tens)

Count the quarters first since they have the biggest cent-value.

1. How much money? Write the amount in cents.

| | |
|---|---|
| **a.**  | **b.**  |
| **c.**  | **d.**  |
| **e.**  | **f.**  |
| **g.**  | **h.**  |
| **i.**  | **j.**  |

2. Are the cent values equal? If not, draw a coin(s) to one side to make them equal.

**a.**

**b.**

178

3. Draw coins to make these money amounts in two ways.

| a. 41¢ (one way) | 41¢ (another way) | b. 62¢ (one way) | 62¢ (another way) |
|---|---|---|---|
| | | | |

4. Cross out the coins you need to buy the item. Write how many cents you have left.

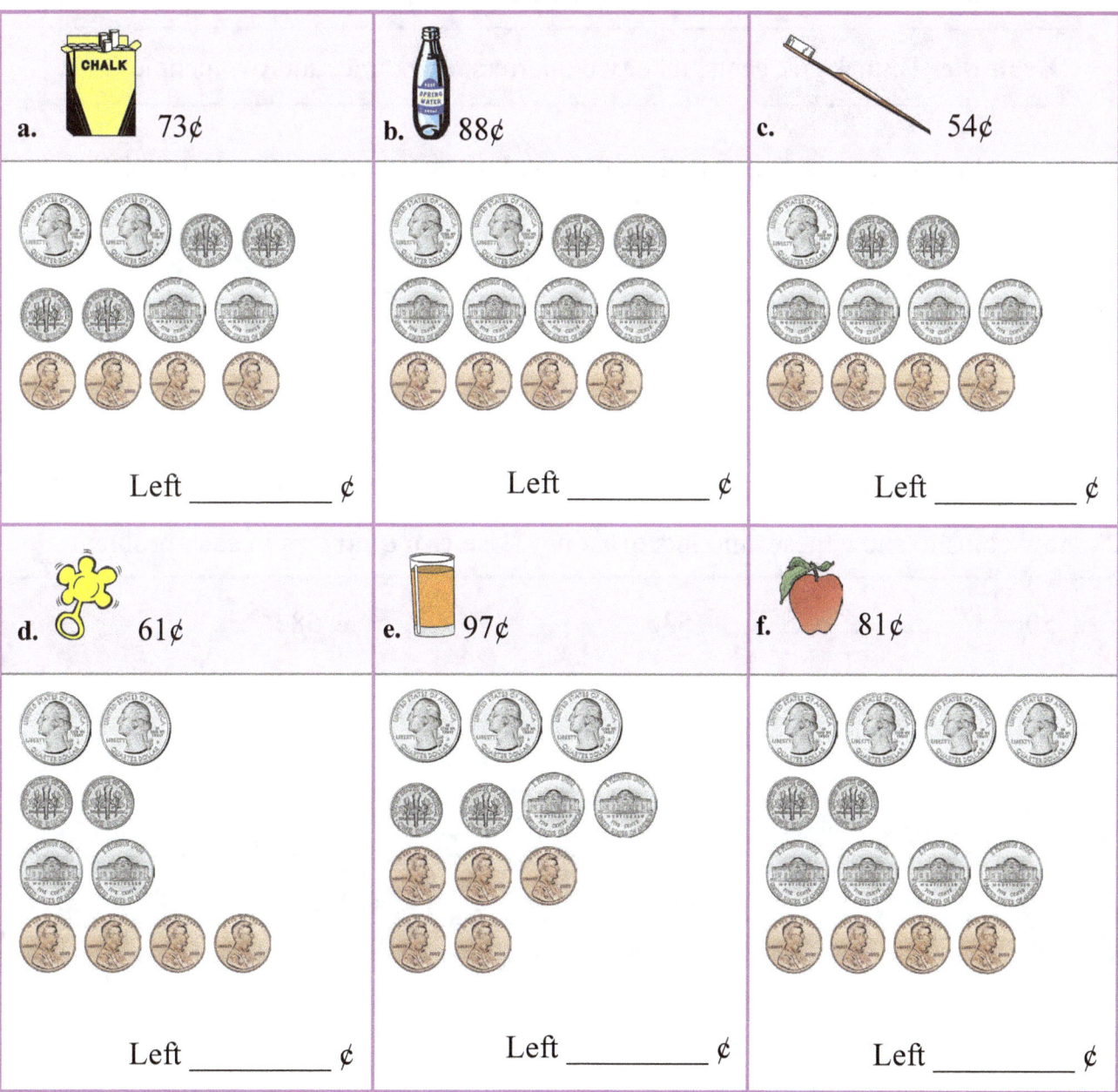

a. CHALK    73¢

Left _____ ¢

b. 88¢

Left _____ ¢

c. 54¢

Left _____ ¢

d. 61¢

Left _____ ¢

e. 97¢

Left _____ ¢

f. 81¢

Left _____ ¢

# Practicing with Money

- **One quarter** = _____ cents.
  Use ONE quarter when the money amount is between 25 and 50 cents.

- **Two quarters** = _____ cents.
  Use TWO quarters when the money amount is between 50 and 75 cents.

- **Three quarters** = _____ cents.
  Use THREE quarters when the money amount is between 75 and 100 cents.

- **Four quarters** = 100 cents or one dollar.

**Example.** To make 62 cents, take two quarters, one dime, and two pennies.

1. Draw coins to show these amounts of money. Use **one quarter** in each problem.

| a.  30¢ | b. 41¢ | c. 48¢ |
|---|---|---|
|  |  |  |

2. Draw coins to show these amounts of money. Use **two quarters** in each problem.

| a.  50¢ | b. 53¢ | c. 58¢ |
|---|---|---|
|  |  |  |
| d. 60¢ | e. 66¢ | f. 72¢ |
|  |  |  |

3. Draw coins to show these amounts of money. Use **three quarters** in each problem.

| a.  80¢ | b. 92¢ | c. 78¢ |
|---|---|---|
|  |  |  |

4. Are the cent values equal? If not, draw a coin(s) to one side to make them equal.

a.  =

b.  =

5. How much is the total if you have:

| a. two dimes and a quarter | b. two quarters, three dimes, seven pennies |
|---|---|
|  |  |

6. Cross out the coins you need to buy the item. Write how many cents you have left.

| a.  76¢ | b.  95¢ | c.  69¢ |
|---|---|---|
|   |  |  |
| Left _____ ¢ | Left _____ ¢ | Left _____ ¢ |

181

# Chapter 10 Mixed Review

1. **a.** Count how many of each flower there are, and then make a bar graph.

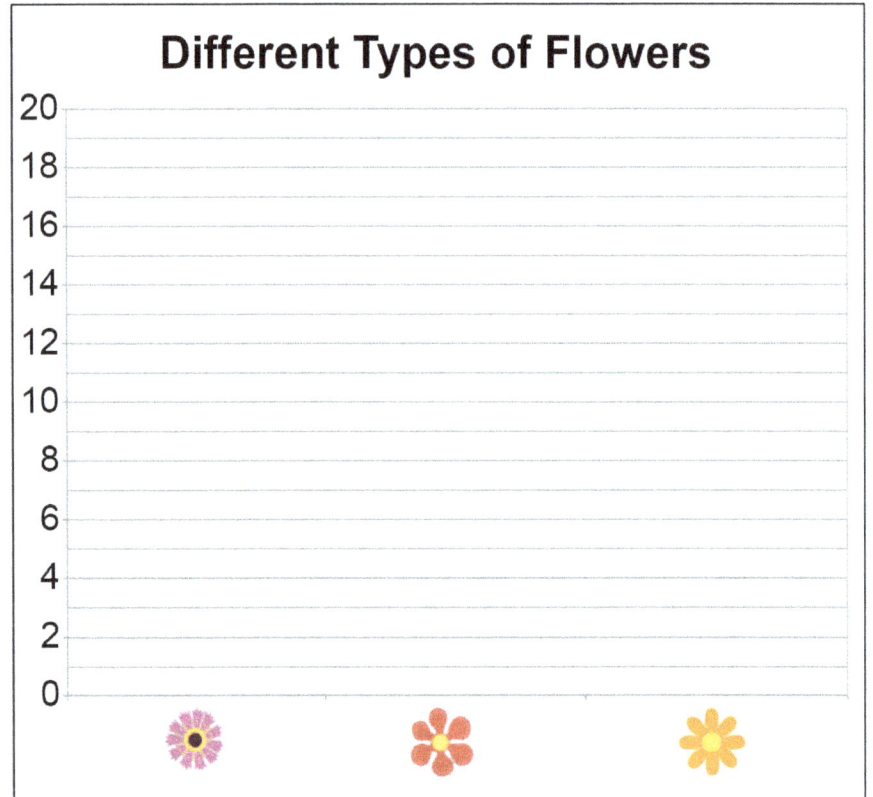

**b.** How many more s are there than ?

**c.** How many flowers are there in total?

2. The graph shows how many books some children read.

| Books that Children Read | |
|---|---|
| Janet | 🕮🕮🕮🕮🕮🕮🕮🕮 |
| Jim | 🕮🕮🕮 |
| Jose | 🕮🕮🕮🕮🕮🕮🕮 |

**a.** Who read the fewest books?

**b.** How many more books did Janet read than Jim?

**c.** How many books did the children read altogether?

**d.** Make your own question about the graph, and answer it!

3. Add. Tell which idea you use to add.

Trick with nine

**a.** $6 + 7 =$ _____  **b.** $4 + 9 =$ _____  Doubles facts

Trick with eight

**c.** $8 + 8 =$ _____  **d.** $3 + 8 =$ _____  Just one more than a double

"Just one more" than a sum with 10

**e.** $6 + 5 =$ _____  **f.** $8 + 9 =$ _____  I just know it!

**g.** $9 + 2 =$ _____  **h.** $7 + 7 =$ _____

4. Add.

| | |
|---|---|
| **a.**    2 tens     6 ones<br>    + 4 tens     6 ones<br>―――――――――――――<br><br>      tens       ones = _____ | **b.**    7 tens     4 ones<br>    + 1 tens     7 ones<br>―――――――――――――<br><br>      tens       ones = _____ |
| **c.**    5 tens     8 ones<br>    + 2 tens     7 ones<br>―――――――――――――<br><br>      tens       ones = _____ | **d.**    3 tens     9 ones<br>    + 3 tens     9 ones<br>―――――――――――――<br><br>      tens       ones = _____ |

5. Measure these lines with a centimeter-ruler.

a. _____ cm

b. _____ cm

c. _____ cm

d. _____ cm

6. Subtract. Think of addition. Choose three colors that go well together to color the boxes with the problems. Write the names of your colors on the lines below.

If the answer is 5, use _____

If the answer is 6, use _____

If the answer is 7, use _____

| | | | |
|---|---|---|---|
| $11 - 6 = $ _____ | $13 - 6 = $ _____ | $12 - 6 = $ _____ | $14 - 9 = $ _____ |
| $14 - 8 = $ _____ | $12 - 7 = $ _____ | $12 - 5 = $ _____ | $16 - 10 = $ _____ |
| $15 - 8 = $ _____ | $13 - 7 = $ _____ | $13 - 8 = $ _____ | $14 - 7 = $ _____ |

7. Draw a line to the correct answer.

| | | | | |
|---|---|---|---|---|
| **8** | 4 + 1 + 2 | **10** | 8 − 1 − 1 | **5** |
| | 2 + 3 + 3 | | 2 + 2 + 2 | |
| | 0 + 6 + 3 | | 10 − 2 − 3 | |
| **9** | 1 + 4 + 3 | **7** | 1 + 3 + 3 | **6** |
| | 2 + 5 + 3 | | 9 − 2 − 2 | |

8. Solve.

**a.** Sofia saw two chickens in her neighbor's yard. Then in another corner of the yard she saw three more! And then under a bush, three more yet!
How many chickens did Sofia see in the neighbor's yard?

**b.** Rich found 8 seashells on the beach, and his brother Mason found 13.
How many more seashells did Mason find than Rich?

**c.** Naomi and Amir also picked seashells on the beach. Amir found 15.
Naomi found three less than Amir. How many did Naomi find?

9. Fill in the skip-counting worms!

a.

b.

c.

d.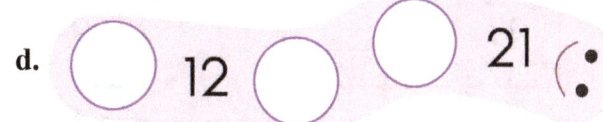

10. Draw coins to show these amounts of money. Use **two or three quarters** in each problem.

| **a.** 60¢ | **b.** 55¢ | **c.** 90¢ |
| --- | --- | --- |
| | | |

11. Are the cent values equal? If not, draw a coin(s) to one side to make them equal.

a.

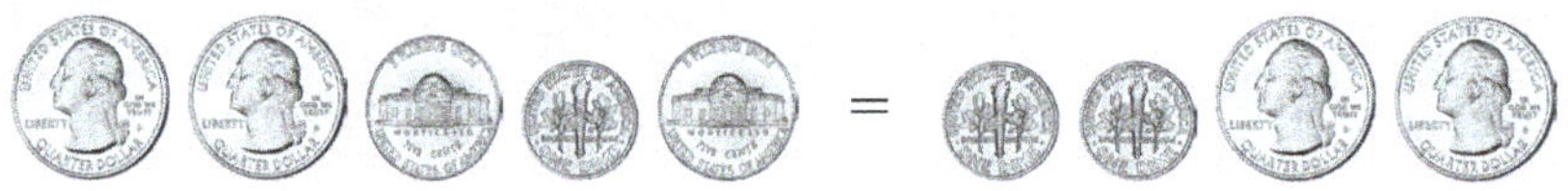

=

b.

=

**Puzzle Corner**  Add the same number in each column.

| +2 | | +3 | | +4 | |
| --- | --- | --- | --- | --- | --- |
| 8 | 10 | 9 | ____ | 7 | ____ |
| 18 | ____ | 19 | ____ | 17 | ____ |
| 38 | ____ | 59 | ____ | 47 | ____ |
| 68 | ____ | 69 | ____ | 77 | ____ |
| 98 | ____ | 89 | ____ | 97 | ____ |

# Chapter 10 Review

1. How much money? Write the amount in cents.

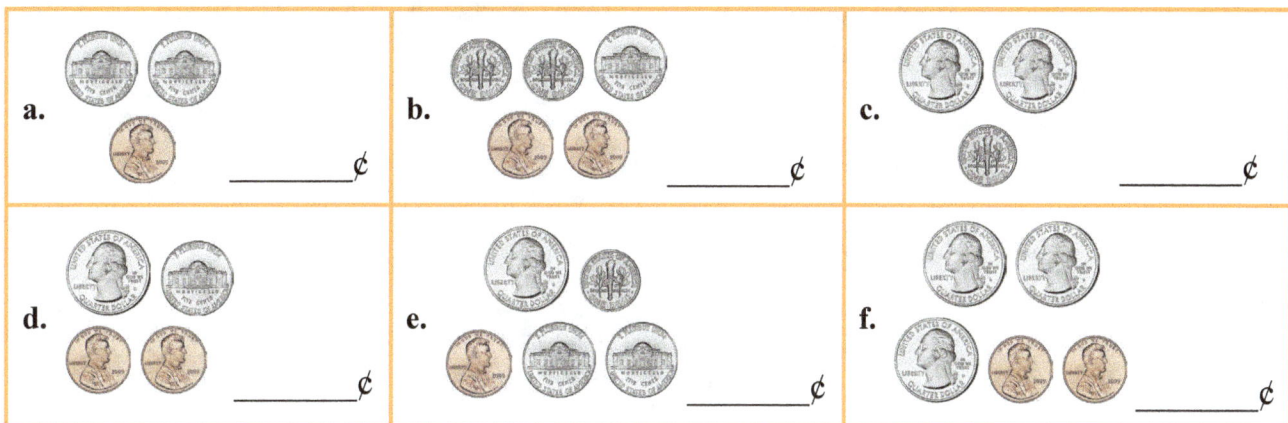

a. _____¢

b. _____¢

c. _____¢

d. _____¢

e. _____¢

f. _____¢

2. Draw coins to illustrate these amounts of money.

| a. 52¢ | b. 27¢ | c. 76¢ |
|---|---|---|
| d. 85¢ | e. 79¢ | f. 34¢ |

3. You buy an item. How much money will you have left?

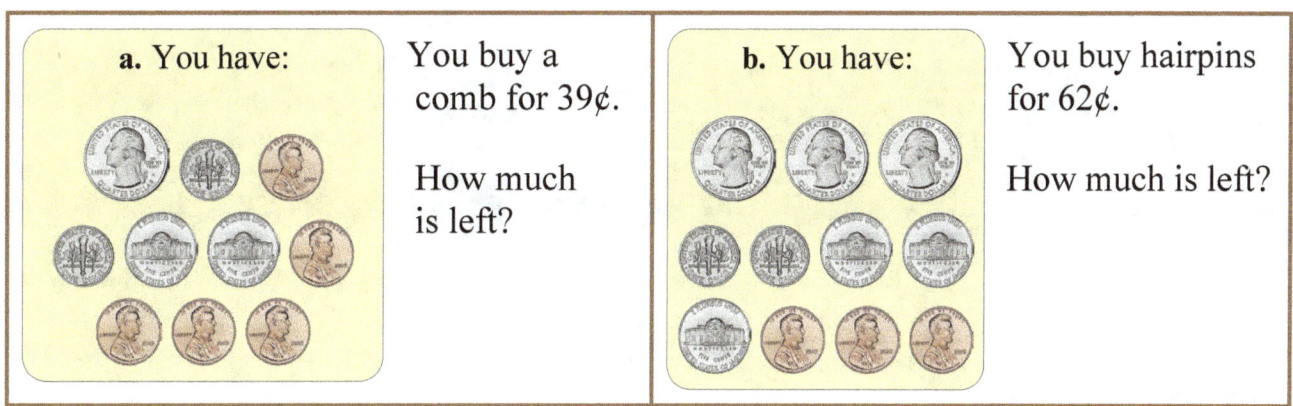

a. You have:    You buy a comb for 39¢.

How much is left?

b. You have:    You buy hairpins for 62¢.

How much is left?

www.ingramcontent.com/pod-product-compliance
Lightning Source LLC
Chambersburg PA
CBHW081451190526
45286CB00016B/1218